This series of practice papers is intended to strengthen your understanding of the topics covered in the Programme of Study for Key Stage 3 Science. It will help you to prepare for the two National Curriculum Tests in Science, which you will undertake at the end of Year 9.

There are three sets of practice papers in this book (six papers in total). You will find the mark schemes in a separate section inserted at the centre.

These practice papers have been designed to perfectly reflect the style and format of the questions in the National Curriculum Tests. They are a useful resource and invaluable revision aid that will help to boost your confidence and reinforce your learning in the build up to your exams.

Each National Curriculum Test in Science will last for one hour and these practice papers have been designed to take roughly the same length of time. However, I would suggest that you try to complete each practice test, no matter how long it takes, to enable you to get the most from each paper. The papers cover all the aspects of the science curriculum that will be tested, including:

- cells and cell functions, nutrition, respiration, and health
- solids, liquids and gases, elements, compounds and mixtures, chemical reactions, geological changes and metals
- physical processes such as electricity and magnetism, forces and motion, light and sound, and the solar system

Everything on the Programme of Study for Key Stage 3 is covered in our bestselling revision guide, The Essentials of Key Stage 3 Science.

Practice papers for Tier 5-7 are also available.

Good luck in your tests.

Katie Whelan

Sc

KEY STAGE
3

TIER
3-6

Science test

Paper 1A

Please read this page carefully but do not open the booklet until you are told to start. Write your name and the name of your school in the spaces below.

First name Hamna

Last name Wahid

School name Brentford School for girls

Remember

- The test is 1 hour long.
- You should have the following things on your desk: pen, pencil, rubber, ruler, protractor and calculator.
- The easier questions are at the beginning of the test.
- Try your best to answer all of the questions.
- The marks available for each question are shown below the mark boxes at the side of each question.
- Do not use rough paper. Write your answers and any working on the paper itself.
- Don't forget to check your work carefully.
- Ask your teacher if you are unsure about anything.

Total marks	76/90

For marker's use only

-14

Lonsdale

11/6/2011

1. The diagrams below show 5 different animals

Salmon

Spider

Mouse

Frog

Lobster

(a) Which of these animals have backbones?

salmon, mouse, frog

1 1a
1 mark

(b) What is the name given to animals without backbones?

invertebrates

1 1b
1 mark

(c) Which of the animals above is an amphibian?

frog

1 1c
1 mark

(d) Which of these animals is a mammal?

mouse

1 1d
1 mark

(e) Which of the four characteristics listed below applies only to mammals?

(i) They lay eggs ☐

(ii) They give birth to live young ✓

(iii) They have hair ✓

(iv) They must return to water to breed ☐

1 1e
1 mark

(f) Describe one way in which the salmon is suited to moving through water.

It has gills / fins to help it breathe underwater

1 1f
1 mark

Maximum 6 marks

2. (a) Below are six changes that occur during adolescence. For each change write down whether the change happens to girls or boys or to both girls and boys.

Change that occurs during adolescence	Girls/boys/both
Hips get broader	Girls
Pubic and underarm hair grows	Both
Voice becomes deeper	Boys
Stronger body smell	Both
Breasts start to develop	Girls
Facial hair grows	Boys

3 2a
3 marks

(b) In girls, what do the ovaries start to produce during adolescence?

eggs

1 2b
1 mark

(c) In boys, what do the testes start to produce during adolescence?

sperm

1 2c
1 mark

(d) During adolescence there is often friction with parents or guardians. Which of the following is the reason for this? Tick the correct box.

(i) The teenager is physically immature but emotionally mature ☐

(ii) The teenager is both physically and emotionally mature ☑

(iii) The teenager is physically mature but emotionally immature ☐

0 2d
1 mark

Maximum 6 marks

3. The diagram below shows the position of the Earth relative to the sun.

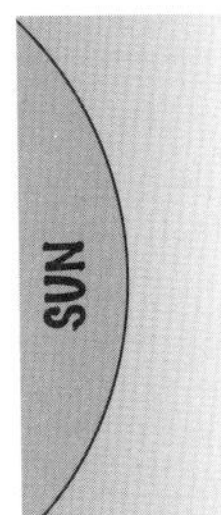

(a) Which season is the Northern hemisphere experiencing?

autemn / winter

3a 1 mark

(b) On the diagram, mark with an X a place which is experiencing night time

3b 1 mark

(c) Delete the incorrect option from the sentence below:

In winter, the sun appears to be **higher/lower** in the sky

3c 1 mark

(d) How long does it take for the Earth to complete one full rotation on its axis?

One day	✓
One month	
One year	

3d 1 mark

(e) How long does it take for the Earth to complete one full orbit of the sun?

One day	
One month	
One year	✓

3e 1 mark

(f) How long does it take for the moon to complete an orbit of the Earth?

One day	
One month	✓
One year	

3f 1 mark

Maximum 6 marks

4. (a) The statements below are about sound. Tick the ones that you think are correct.

(i) Sound is a form of energy	✓
(ii) Sound needs a material to travel through	✓
(iii) Sound is a source of energy	✓
(iv) Loudness depends on frequency	
(v) Pitch depends on amplitude	✓
(vi) Sound travels faster than light	✓
(vii) Humans can hear all sounds	
(viii) We hear sounds because our eardrum vibrates	

3 4a
4 marks

(b)

A B

(i) Which of the sounds above has the highest frequency?

A

1 4bi
1 mark

(ii) Which of the sounds above has the biggest amplitude?

B

1 4bii
1 mark

Maximum 6 marks

5. The drawings below show the particular use of different substances in different objects.

(a) Draw a line from each substance to the characteristic that makes it suitable for that use. Draw only four lines.

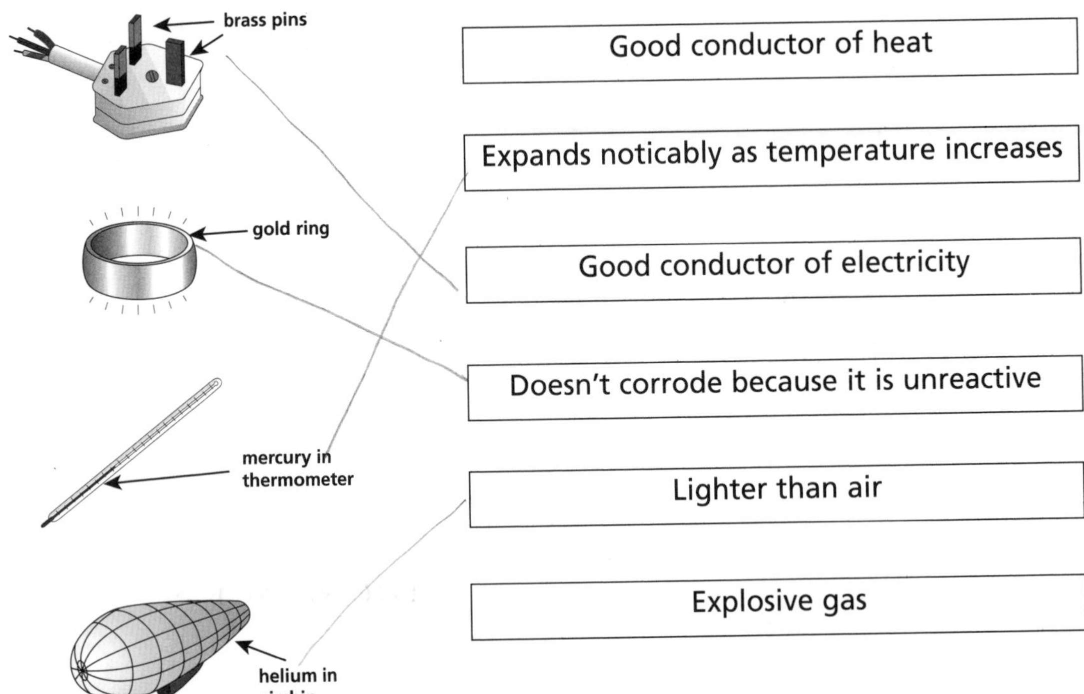

4 | 5a
4 marks

(b) Which one of the four substances named above is not an element?

brass

1 | 5b
1 mark

(c) Which one of the four substances named above is not a metal?

helium is not a metal but is a gas

1 | 5c
1 mark

Maximum 6 marks

6. (a) The teacher in Jack's class set up a distillation demonstration. The liquid in the flask was salt water solution which was heated up until it gently boiled.

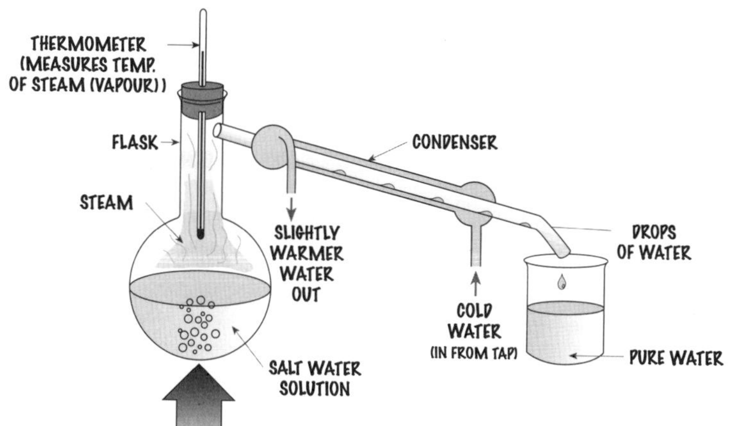

(i) Why would the temperature of the thermometer read 100°C?

because 100°c is boiling temp

1 mark 6ai: 1

(ii) What happens to the steam when it reaches the condenser?

It will condense into water vapour

1 mark 6aii: 1

(iii) What would be left in the flask if the salt water solution was boiled until there was no liquid left?

salt would be left behind

1 mark 6aiii: 1

(b) The method above can also be used to separate a mixture of alcohol and water. Alcohol is a liquid that boils at 78°C.

(i) What temperature reading would the thermometer show if this mixture was heated until it gently boiled?

73°c (78)

1 mark 6bi: 0

(ii) Which liquid would be collected in the beaker?

water (Alcohol)

1 mark 6bii: 0

(iii) Which liquid would be left behind in the flask?

alcohol (Water)

1 mark 6biii: 0

Maximum 6 marks

7. The diagram below shows part of the periodic table. It includes the names of the common elements.

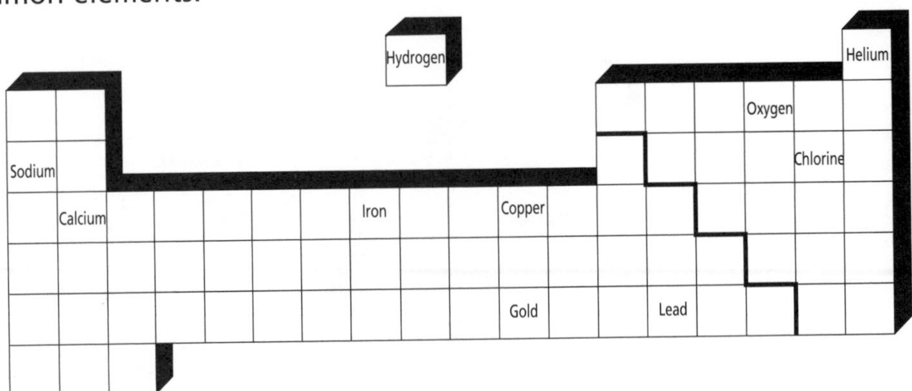

(a) The elements are arranged in order of increasing mass of atom. Which element is made up of the lightest atom?

Helium

0 7a
1 mark

(b) All elements are either metals or non-metals. Complete the table below by writing the names of the elements that are included in the periodic table above in the correct columns.

Metal elements	Non-metal elements
Lead	Calcium
Gold	Oxygen
copper	Chlorine
Iron	Helium
	Sodium
	Hydrogen

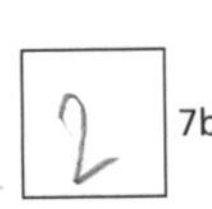
2 7b
3 marks

(c) Give the name of one of the elements in the table above which is a poor conductor of electricity.

Calcium

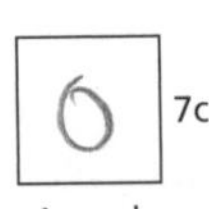
0 7c
1 mark

(d) Give the name of the one element in the table above which is magnetic.

Iron

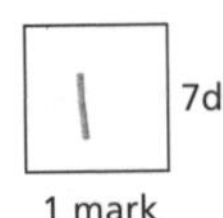
1 7d
1 mark

Maximum 6 marks

8. (a) Hefin and Ian were looking at cells under the microscope. They thought that they were looking at plant cells because of the following reasons. Indicate whether the statements were true or false by placing a 'T' or an 'F' in the boxes alongside.

"There is a membrane so it's a plant cell."	F
"We can't see a nucleus so it's a plant cell."	F
"There are chloroplasts so it's a plant cell."	T
"It must be a plant cell because it has cytoplasm."	T

1 8a
2 marks

(b) Hefin and Ian added iodine to the material under the microscope and it changed colour from pale brown to blue-black.

(i) What does this colour change indicate?

A physical reaction has taken place and it is An alkali

0 8bi
1 mark

(ii) Does this support their claim that they were looking at plant cells?

No

0 8bii
1 mark

(c) Name two types of specialised plant cells.

1 epitheleal

2 root steam

0 8c
1 mark

(d) Name two types of specialised animal cells.

1 red blood cells

2 sperm

1 8d
1 mark

Maximum 6 marks

9. Grace and Katie measured the heights of people in their class and produced the following bar chart.

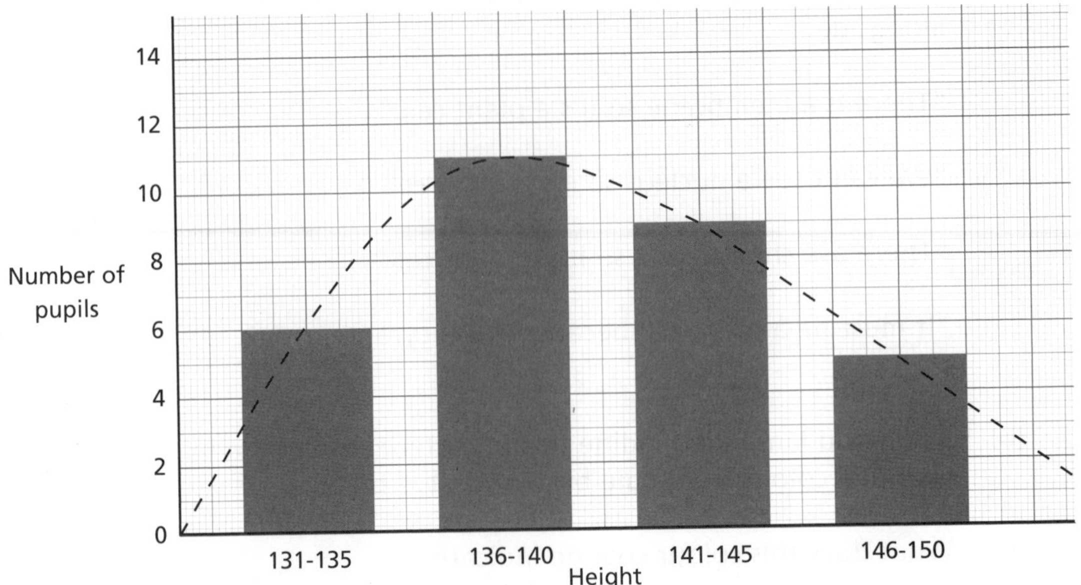

(a)(i) What units of measurement were used to measure the height of the class?

cm centimetres

1 mark 9ai

(ii) How many people were in the 146-150 range?

5

1 mark 9aii

(iii) How many people were in the class?

31

1 mark 9aiii

(b) The dotted line shows the overall shape of their bar chart. If they investigated the following characteristics, which would produce a similar shape to the first bar chart?

(i) Weight ☑ (ii) Eye colour ☐

(iii) Intelligence ☑ (iv) Hair colour ☐

2 marks 9b

(c) Weight is a characteristic which:

(i) Depends totally on inherited factors ☐

(ii) Depends totally on environmental factors ☑

(iii) Depends on both inherited and environmental factors ☐

1 mark 9c

Maximum 6 marks

10. (a) Beverley and Paul left a box of toys on the lawn for a few days and when they moved the box they were astonished to find that the grass underneath had turned yellow.

(i) What substance causes the green colour in plants?

chloroplast

10ai 1 mark

(ii) Why was this substance missing from the grass which had been under the toy box?

there was no Sunlight (photosynthesis)

10aii 1 mark

(iii) Explain what would happen to the yellow grass over the next few days.

It would recover and turn back green

10aiii 1 mark

(b) Paul suggested that a clear plastic sheet would have the same effect, so he pegged it onto the lawn and left it for a few days.

(i) Would you expect the grass to become yellow?

No

10bi 1 mark

(ii) Explain your answer to (i) above.

It would still get sunlight but no water

10bii 1 mark

(c) What is the name of the process by which green plants make glucose using the energy from the sun?

Photosynthesis

10c 1 mark

Maximum 6 marks

11. Elliott holds a ball at the top of a ramp.

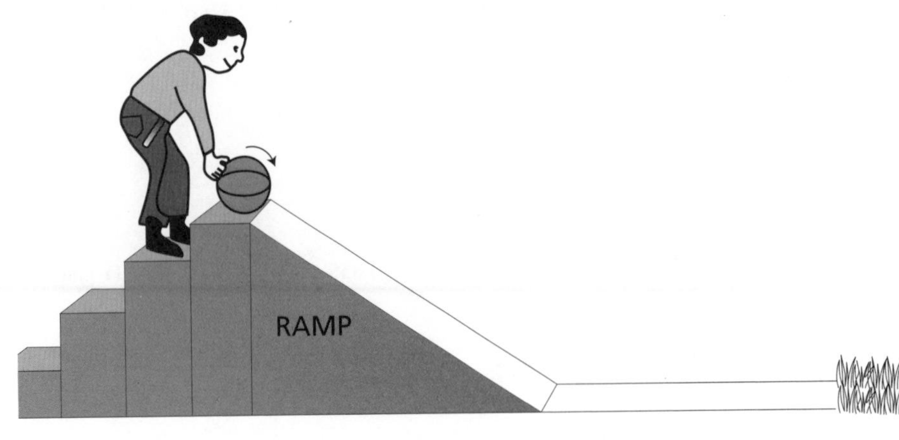

(a) What type of energy does the ball have when it is at the top of the ramp?

friction / none

0 | 11a | 1 mark

(b) What type of energy is this converted to when the ball is rolling down the ramp?

Kinetic

1 | 11b | 1 mark

(c) Elliott lets the ball roll down the ramp. What force is acting on it to cause it to roll down the ramp?

Gravity

1 | 11c | 1 mark

(d) When the ball meets the ground it is travelling 2m/s. If the ball continues to travel at the same speed, how far will it travel in 4 seconds?

8 m/s

1 | 11d | 1 mark

(e) The ball then rolls over some grass. What happens to its speed and why?

It slows down because the grass creates fiction

2 | 11e | 2 marks

Maximum 6 marks

12. The diagram below shows a simple circuit that Sam has connected.

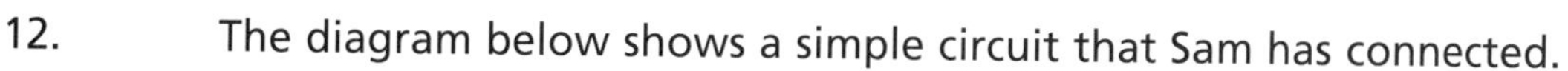

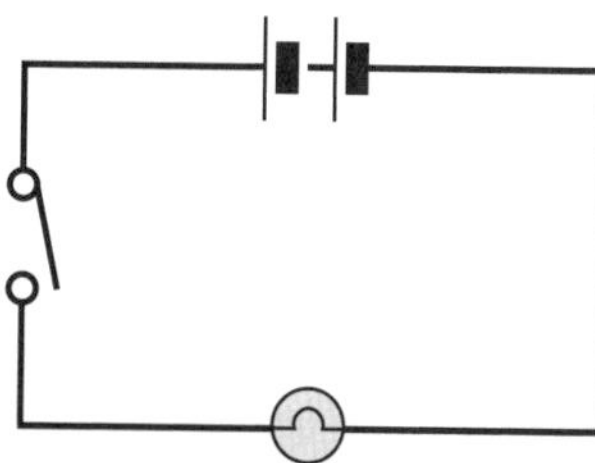

(a) What does Sam need to do in order to turn the bulb on?

Close the swith

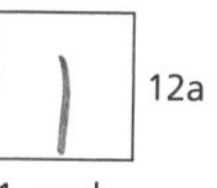

1 | 12a

1 mark

(b) Sam inserts another bulb into the circuit, as shown in the diagram below.

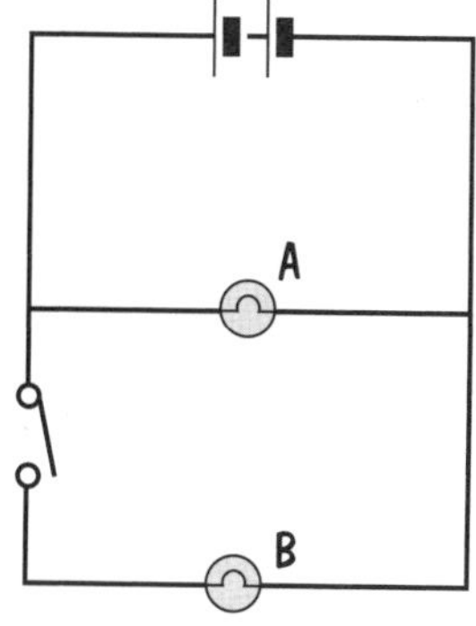

(i) Is the new circuit a series or a parallel circuit?

Parallel

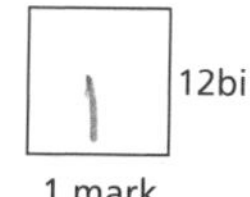

1 | 12bi

1 mark

(ii) Put a tick in the boxes next to the statements that are true for this circuit.

Both bulbs will be on all the time	
Bulb A will be on all the time	 ✓
Bulb B will be on all the time	
Bulb B will be on only when the switch is closed	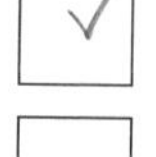 ✓
Both bulbs will be off all the time	

2 | 12bii

2 marks

(iii) If 0.4 amps flows from the cell in the circuit in part (b), how many amps would flow through each of the two bulbs, assuming they were identical bulbs?

0.8 amps

2 | 12biii

2 marks

Maximum 6 marks

13. Look at the diagram below.

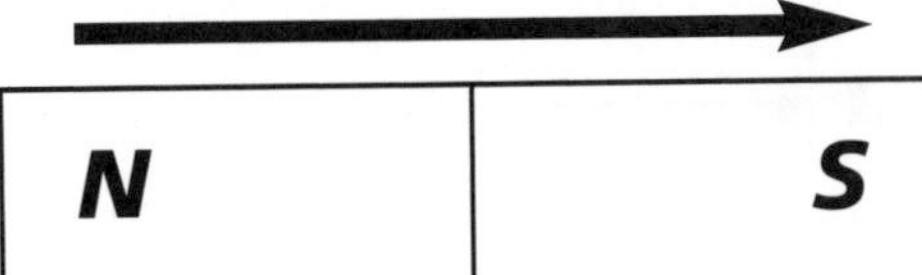

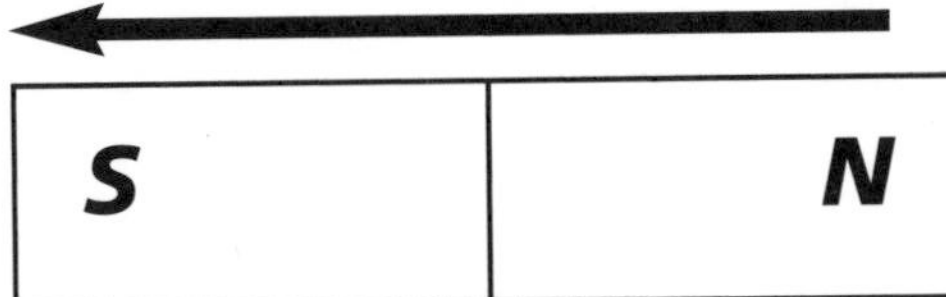

(a) If the magnets are brought close together, will they attract or repel each other?

Repel

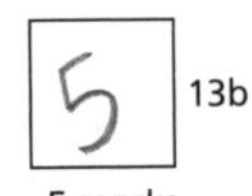

1 13a

1 mark

(b) Insert the words below into the gaps in the following sentences.

iron **South** **magnetic field** **North** **plastic**

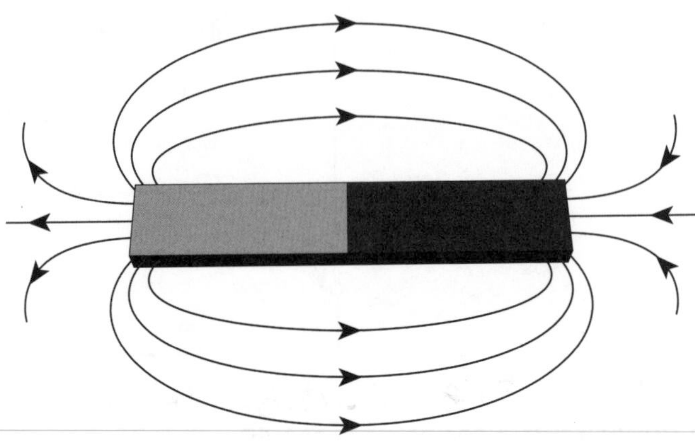

Magnets have a region of space around them called a magnetic field.

They have two poles, which are North and south.

They can attract magnetic materials. One magnetic material is Iron.

Magnets have no effect on non-magnetic materials, such as plastic.

5 13b

5 marks

Maximum 6 marks

14. Grace and Imogen performed an investigation into how different acids react with limestone (calcium carbonate).

They set up the equipment as shown and then conducted several experiments using the following different acids: vinegar, lemon juice, dilute hydrochloric acid and dilute sulphuric acid.

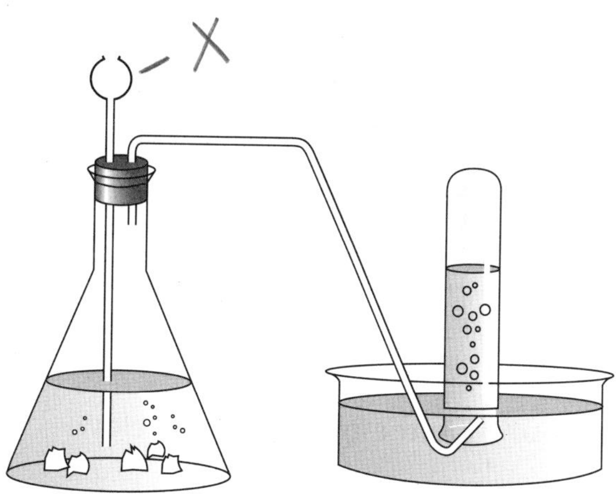

(a) Label with an X the piece of apparatus through which the acid is added. 1 14a 1 mark

(b) What is being measured in this experiment?

The acidity of different materials

1 14b 1 mark

(c) Describe one piece of evidence which tells you that a chemical reaction is occurring.

Blubbles (gas)

1 14c 1 mark

(d) Name two things which would have to be kept constant in order to make this a fair test.

1 amount of acid added

2 amount of water added

1 14d 2 marks

(e) Name a gas which dissolves in rain to make it acidic.

carbon dioxide

1 14e 1 mark

Maximum 6 marks

15. James and Thomas carried out an experiment to investigate how the solubility of sugar changes with temperature. Sugar was added to the water until no more dissolved.

Temperature of water (°C)	Amount of sugar dissolved (g)
0	0
10	15
20	31
30	45
40	60
50	76
60	93

(a) Plot these results on the graph paper below.

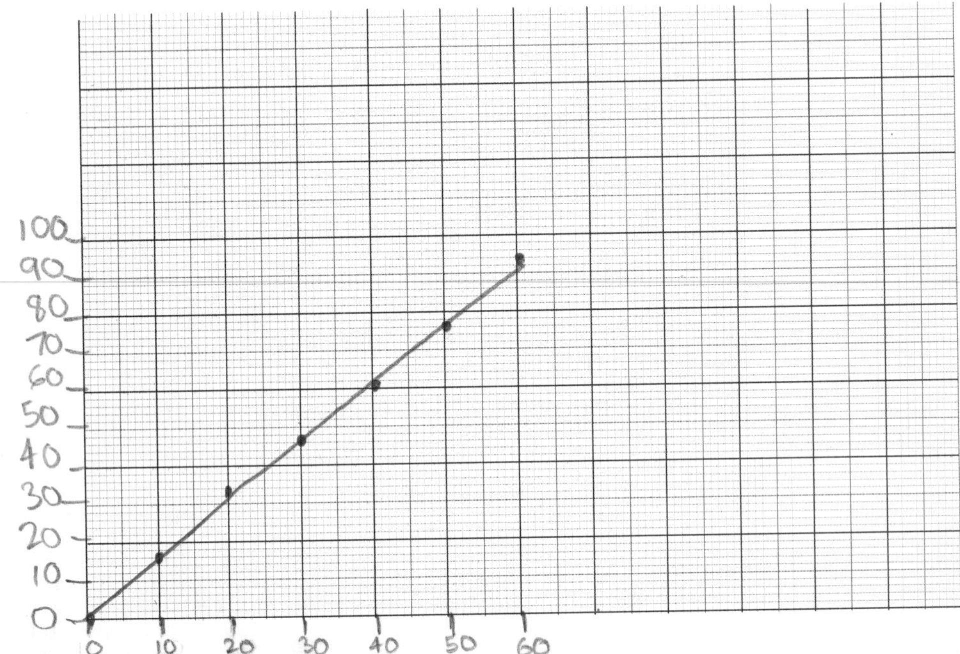

3 15a
3 marks

(b) Why did no sugar dissolve at 0°C?

The water was too cold for the sugar to dissolve

1 15b
1 mark

(c) How much sugar would dissolve at 35°C?

50g

1 15c
1 mark

(d) Which substance in this experiment was the solvent?

water

1 15d
1 mark

Maximum 6 marks

Sc

KEY STAGE
3

TIER
3-6

Science test

Paper 2A

Please read this page carefully but do not open the booklet until you are told to start. Write your name and the name of your school in the spaces below.

First name ______________________________

Last name ______________________________

School name ______________________________

Remember

- The test is 1 hour long.
- You should have the following things on your desk: pen, pencil, rubber, ruler, protractor and calculator.
- The easier questions are at the beginning of the test.
- Try your best to answer all of the questions.
- The marks available for each question are shown below the mark boxes at the side of each question.
- Do not use rough paper. Write your answers and any working on the paper itself.
- Don't forget to check your work carefully.
- Ask your teacher if you are unsure about anything.

Total marks	

For marker's use only

Lonsdale

1. The diagram below shows a food web.

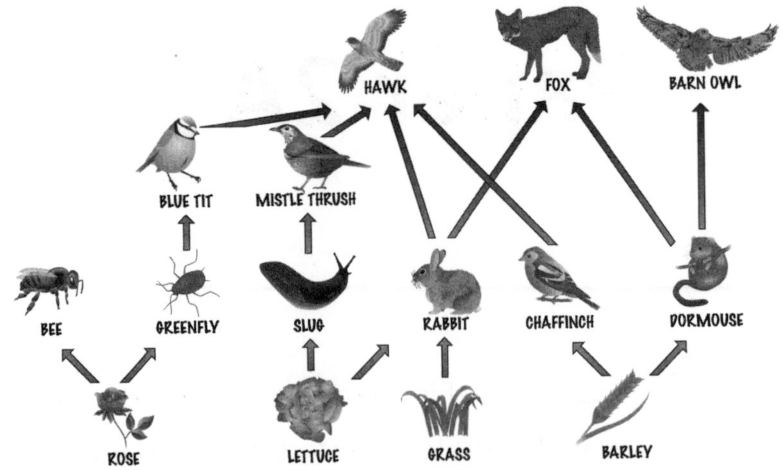

(a)(i) Which of the following is a producer: grass, rabbit or fox?

grass

1ai — 1 mark

(ii) Which of the following is a carnivore: grass, rabbit or fox?

fox

1aii — 1 mark

(iii) Which of the following is a herbivore: grass, rabbit or fox?

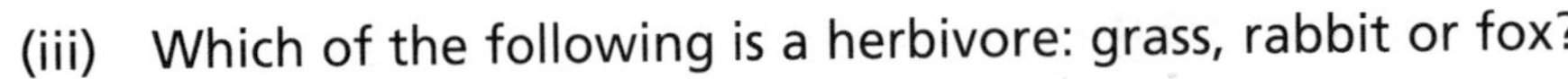

rabbit

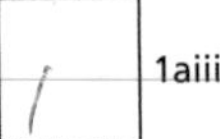

1aiii — 1 mark

(b) Complete the following food chains which can be found in the food web above.

(i) Rose ⟶ greenfly ⟶ Blue tit ⟶ hawk

1bi — 1 mark

(ii) rabbit ⟶ slug ⟶ mistle thrush ⟶ hawk

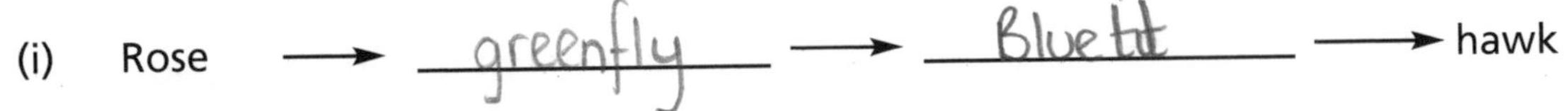

1bii — 1 mark

(c) In the food web above, which consumer do the fox and barn owl compete for?

doormouse

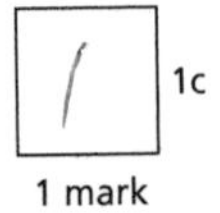

1c — 1 mark

Maximum 6 marks

2. The diagram shows the four things that are needed and the two things that are produced during photosynthesis.

(a) Which one is obtained from the soil?

water

2a — 1 mark

(b) Which one is obtained from the sun?

light

2b — 1 mark

(c) Which one is used for biomass and energy?

glucose

2c — 1 mark

(d) Which one is found in leaves?

chlorophyll

2d — 1 mark

(e) Which one is obtained from the air?

carbon dioxide

2e — 1 mark

(f) Which one is released to the atmosphere?

oxygen

2f — 1 mark

Maximum 6 marks

3. Draw lines to connect each process below to the correct change of state. Draw four lines only.

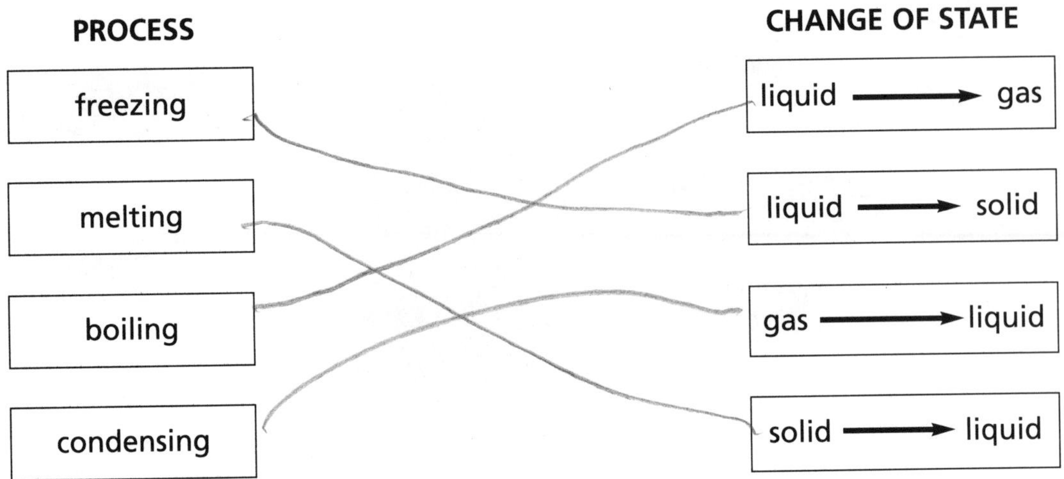

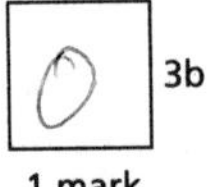
3a
4 marks

(b) When a solid or liquid is heated it will eventually change state. What happens to the temperature of the substance as it changes state?

it increases

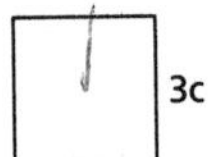
3b
1 mark

(c) What happens to the mass of a substance when it changes state?

it stays the same

3c
1 mark

Maximum 6 marks

4. John has been given two cards. Each card has on it a definition of a particular type of substance.

CARD A

A substance made up of the atoms of two or more elements or the molecules of two or more compounds which have not been joined together in a chemical reaction.

CARD B

A substance formed from the atoms of two or more elements which have been joined together in a chemical reaction.

(a) Which card has the definition of a compound?

B

1 mark 4a — 1

(b) What type of substance does the other card have a definition of?

Solution

1 mark 4b — 1

(c) Here are 10 substances.

water	**milk**	**mineral oil**	**salt**
carbon dioxide	**air**	**sea water**	
iron sulphide	**copper sulphate**	**fizzy pop**	

Write down the names of four compounds from the list above.

1 iron sulphide

2 copper sulphate

3 carbon dioxide

4 salt

4 marks 4c — 4

Maximum 6 marks

5. The table below gives the planets in the solar system in order from the Sun.

Mercury	Venus	Earth	Mars	Jupiter	Saturn	Uranus	Neptune	Pluto

(a)(i) Name a planet that takes longer than one year to go around the Sun.

1 5ai
1 mark

Jupiter

(ii) Why does this planet take longer than one year to go around the Sun?

5aii
1 mark

(b)(i) Name a planet whose surface temperature is higher than Earth's.

5bi
1 mark

(ii) Why is this planet's surface temperature higher than Earth's?

5bii
1 mark

(c)(i) What is the name of the force that keeps Earth and other planets in their orbits?

5ci
1 mark

(ii) What exerts this force on Earth and the other planets?

5cii
1 mark

Maximum 6 marks

6. Natalie is inside when she hears thunder. She looks out of her window so she can see the lightning and hear the thunder.

(a)(i) Tick the box next to the statement that is correct.

She hears the thunder and sees the lightning at the same time ☐

She hears the thunder first ☐

She sees the lightning first ☐

6ai 1 mark

(ii) Explain why.

____

____

6aii 1 mark

(b) Back at school, Natalie carried out a simple experiment. She placed an electric bell inside a bell jar which was connected to a vacuum pump. The bell was switched on.

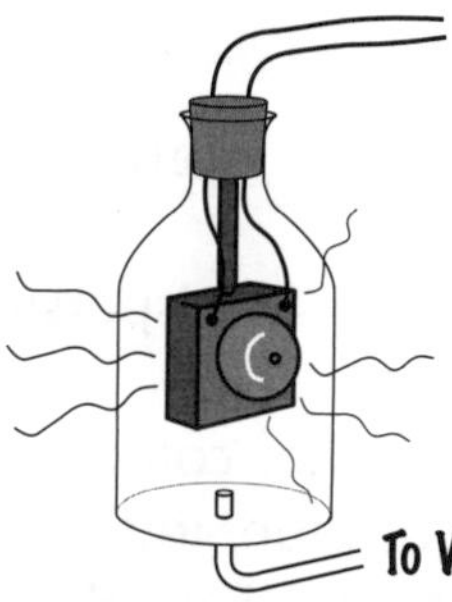

(i) What would Natalie observe if the vacuum pump was switched on and air removed?

____

____

____

6bi 2 marks

(ii) Complete the sentence using the following words.

sound **light** **heat**

__________ and __________ can travel through a vacuum, whereas __________ cannot.

6bii 2 marks

Maximum 6 marks

7. Jeff carried out an experiment where he passed a ray of light through a glass prism. To his astonishment he saw that the ray of light split up into a range of colours with red light at one end and violet light at the other end.

(a) What is the name given to the range of colours that Jeff saw? Tick the box next to the correct answer.

Filtration	☐	Reflection	☐
Spectrum	☐	Dispersion	☐

7a
1 mark

(b) What is the splitting up of white light called? Tick the box next to the correct answer.

Filtration	☐	Reflection	☐
Spectrum	☐	Dispersion	☐

7b
1 mark

(c) Apart from red and violet, the other colours that white light splits up into are (in no particular order): blue, orange, indigo, yellow and green. Complete the following table by writing in these five colours in the correct order.

Red						**Violet**

7c
2 marks

(d) Jeff goes to a disco. He is wearing a red cap, green T-shirt and a pair of blue trousers. Complete the table below to show what colour these garments would appear to be if red light was shone on him at the disco.

Garment	**Colour of garment in red light**
Red cap	
Green T-shirt	
Blue trousers	

7d
2 marks

Maximum 6 marks

8. Diagrams of an animal cell and a plant cell are shown below.

ANIMAL CELL PLANT CELL

(a) Which part of the plant cell is non-living?

____

8a 1 mark

(b) Name two structures which are present in plant cells but not animal cells.

1 ____

2 ____

8b 2 marks

(c) Which structure in both plant cells and animal cells controls the passage of substances into and out of the cell?

____

8c 1 mark

(d) In which structure in plant cells does photosynthesis take place?

____

8d 1 mark

(e) In which part of the cell is cell sap found?

____

8e 1 mark

Maximum 6 marks

9. Look at the animals drawn below.

John Dory Zetek's Frog Skylark

Common Iguana Red Deer

(a) To which large group do all these animals belong?

9a
1 mark

(b) Which one of the animals shown above is a mammal?

9b
1 mark

(c) Give two characteristics of mammals.

1

2

9c
2 marks

(d) Which of the animals shown above breathes through its skin?

9d
1 mark

(e) Which one of the animals shown above has the lightest bones?

9e
1 mark

Maximum 6 marks

10. Nearly a hundred years ago scientists were investigating the ways in which different food types contributed to obesity. They used a group of 30 volunteers who were given various different food types for a period of 3 months.

Group A was given only foods which were high in fat.

Group B was given only foods which were high in protein.

Group C was given only foods which were high in carbohydrates.

(a)(i) List three things the scientists would have to keep the same in order to make this a fair test.

1 ____

2 ____

3 ____ 10ai 3 marks

(ii) Name the one factor that the scientists changed in this experiment (the independent variable).

____ 10aii 1 mark

(b) It was found that people on the high protein diet gained least weight. However, a diet consisting only of protein would not be good for you. Give two reasons why this is so.

1 ____

____

2 ____

____ 10b 2 marks

Maximum 6 marks

11. (a) A student set up the experiment as shown below to investigate the substances breathed out by humans.

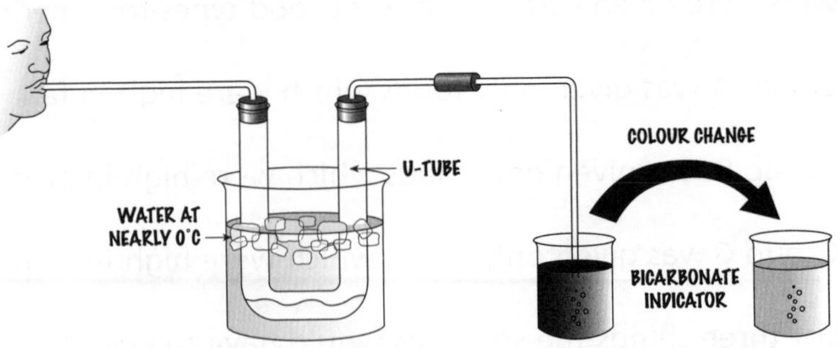

(i) What is the clear substance formed at the bottom of the U-tube?

____

11ai
1 mark

(ii) What substance causes the bicarbonate indicator to change from purple to yellow?

____

11aii
1 mark

(b) The student then set up the following experiment using seeds.

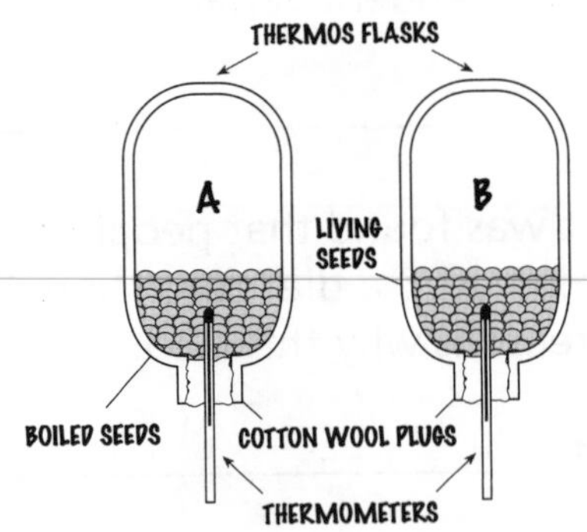

(i) What would you expect to notice about the temperature of the two flasks after 48 hours?

____

11bi
1 mark

(ii) What process would cause this to happen?

____

11bii
1 mark

(iii) Would you expect this to occur in all living things?

Yes ☐ No ☐

11biii
1 mark

(iv) What units would be used to measure the temperature in the flasks?

____

11biv
1 mark

Maximum 6 marks

12. (a) Railway lines have gaps between neighbouring sections of track. These gaps are about 10mm wide.

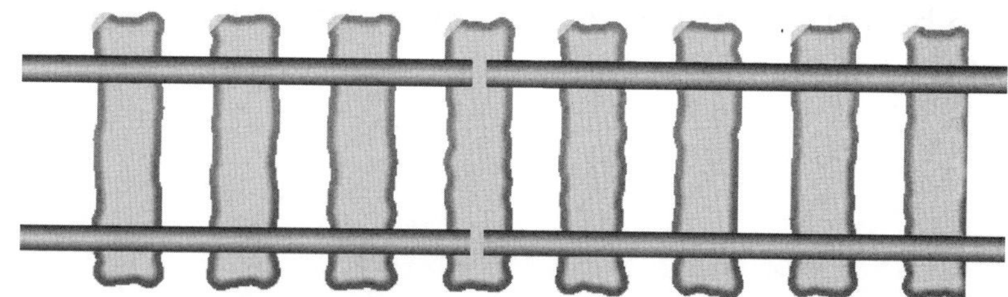

(i) How does the size of objects change as they get hotter?

____ 12ai 1 mark

(ii) As the temperature of the railway line increases, what happens to the gaps between the neighbouring sections of track?

____ 12aii 1 mark

(iii) What problem would be cased by a rise in temperature if there were no gaps between sections?

____ 12aiii 1 mark

(iv) In countries which experience larger variations in temperature, should the gaps be wider or narrower?

____ 12aiv 1 mark

(b)(i) When a train driver applies his brakes, what is it that slows the train down?

____

____

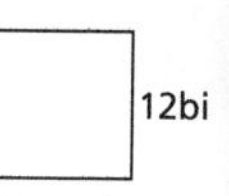

12bi 1 mark

(ii) What effect does this process have on the temperature of the railway lines?

____

____

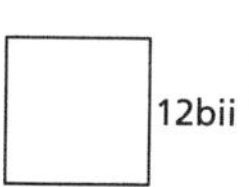

12bii 1 mark

Maximum 6 marks

13. Julie placed a conical flask onto a balance. It weighed 60g. She then added 100g of dilute hydrochloric acid and 5g of calcium carbonate. The total mass of the beaker, the acid and the calcium carbonate was therefore 165g at the start of the reaction.

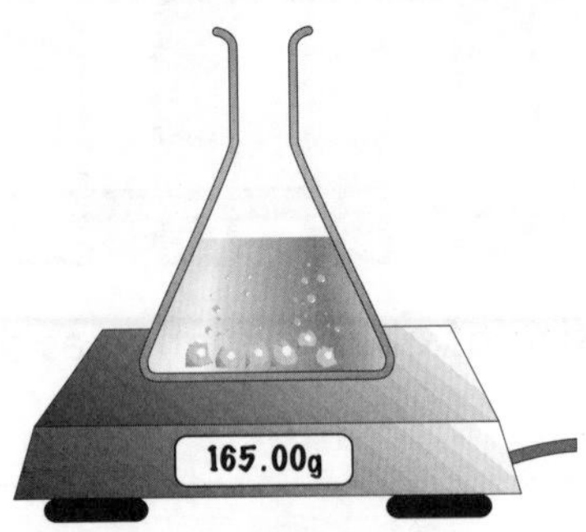

(a) How could Julie tell, by looking, that a chemical reaction was occurring?

13a 1 mark

(b) What would you expect to have happened to the total mass shown on the balance by the end of the reaction?

13b 1 mark

(c) Explain why you think this would have happened.

13c 1 mark

(d) What other change may have occurred in the beaker?

13d 1 mark

(e) Complete the word equation for this reaction.

Calcium carbonate + hydrochloric acid → ☐ + ☐ + ☐

13e 1 mark

(f) Name a naturally occurring substance which is mainly compound of calcium carbonate.

13f 1 mark

Maximum 6 marks

14. This table describes how different metals react when added to water and to hydrochloric acid:

Metal	**Reaction with water**	**Reaction with dilute hydrochloric acid**
Iron	Reacts with steam to produce a gas and iron oxide	Moderate reaction to produce bubbles of gas
Gold	No reaction	No reaction
Sodium	Floats, melts then seems to catch fire due to heat of reaction	Reacts explosively (SHOULD NEVER BE DONE!)
Magnesium	Very slow reaction to produce a gas and magnesium hydroxide	Reacts quickly to produce bubbles of gas

(a) List these metals in order of their reactivity, **starting with the most reactive.**

____

____

____

____

14a
1 mark

(b) Suggest another metal which isn't in this table that reacts in a similar way to sodium.

____

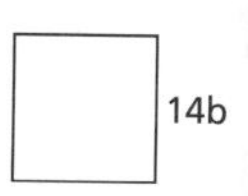
14b
1 mark

(c) In the reactions above, where bubbles of gas are produced, which gas is given off?

____

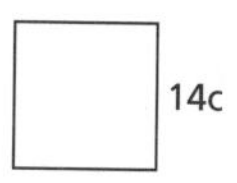
14c
1 mark

(d) Complete the word equation for the reaction between magnesium and dilute hydrochloric acid.

Magnesium + dilute hydrochloric acid ⟶ ______________ + ______________

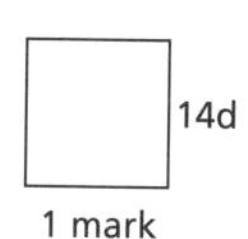
14d
1 mark

(e) Besides bubbles of gas, what other evidence would indicate that a chemical reaction was occurring?

____

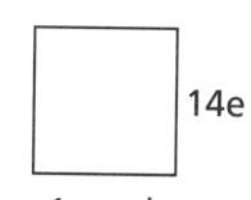
14e
1 mark

(f) Why are reactive metals never found as pure metals but always as ores?

____

____

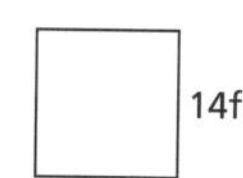
14f
1 mark

Maximum 6 marks

15. After it snowed Sunil and Ian went sledging on the hills. The diagram below shows their sledging route.

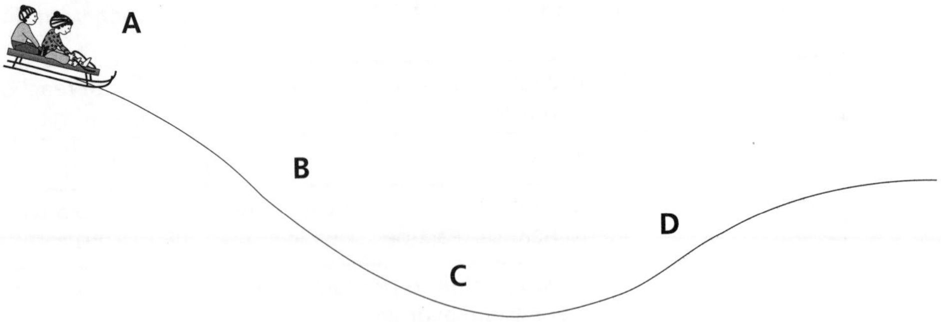

A

B

D

C

(a)(i) At which point would they be travelling fastest?

15ai
1 mark

____

(ii) At which point would they be accelerating?

15aii
1 mark

____

(iii) At which point would they be decelerating?

15aiii
1 mark

____

(b)(i) Name two forces acting on the sledge at point B

1 _______________

2 _______________

15bi
2 marks

(ii) At point C these two forces are balanced. What can you say about their speed at this point?

____

____

15bii
1 mark

Maximum 6 marks

Sc

KEY STAGE
3

TIER
3-6

Science test

Paper 1B

Please read this page carefully but do not open the booklet until you are told to start. Write your name and the name of your school in the spaces below.

First name ________________________________

Last name ________________________________

School name ________________________________

Remember

- The test is 1 hour long.
- You should have the following things on your desk: pen, pencil, rubber, ruler, protractor and calculator.
- The easier questions are at the beginning of the test.
- Try your best to answer all of the questions.
- The marks available for each question are shown below the mark boxes at the side of each question.
- Do not use rough paper. Write your answers and any working on the paper itself.
- Don't forget to check your work carefully.
- Ask your teacher if you are unsure about anything.

Total marks	

For marker's use only

Lonsdale

1. (a) Draw lines from the four food types shown below to the boxes that describe what we use them for.

Proteins	stored energy
Carbohydrates	growth and repair
Fats	healthy bones and teeth
Fibre	energy through respiration
	helps movement through the digestive system

1a 4 marks

(b) The body needs important minerals such as iron and calcium.

(i) How is iron used in the body?

1bi 1 mark

____

(ii) How is calcium used in the body?

1bii 1 mark

____

Maximum 6 marks

2. The diagram shows a baby which is in the birth position.

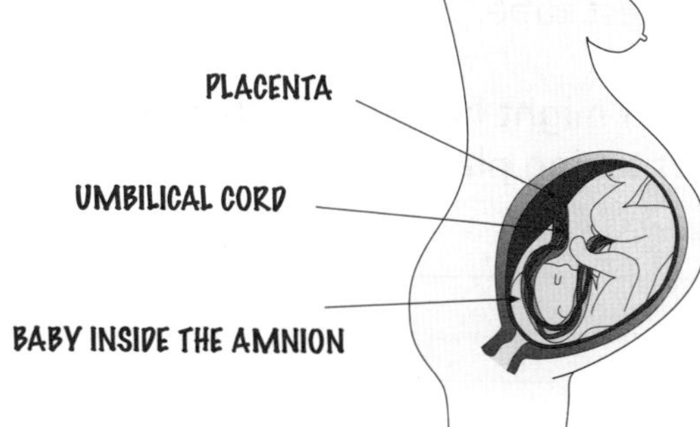

(a) The umbilical cord carries substances between the mother and the baby. Put one tick in each row of the table below to indicate the direction each substance goes.

Substance	From mother to baby	From baby to mother
Oxygen		
Waste		
Carbon dioxide		
Food		

2a
4 marks

(b) What does the umbilical cord attach the baby to?

____

2b
1 mark

(c) The amnion is a sac filled with amniotic fluid, or 'the waters'. What is the purpose of the amniotic fluid?

____

____

2c
1 mark

Maximum 6 marks

3. Stephen and Claire added some strips of magnesium ribbon to dilute hydrochloric acid in a test tube.

(a) Name two things which might happen which would suggest to them that a chemical reaction was taking place.

1 ______________________________

2 ______________________________

3a 2 marks

(b) Which gas is given off in this reaction?

____

3b 1 mark

(c) What colour would dilute hydrochloric acid turn universal indicator?

____

3c 1 mark

(d)(i) Name a substance which could be added to dilute hydrochloric acid to form a neutral solution.

____

3di 1 mark

(ii) What colour would the universal indicator now be?

____

3dii 1 mark

Maximum 6 marks

4. The bar chart shows the pH of five liquids, A, B, C, D and E.

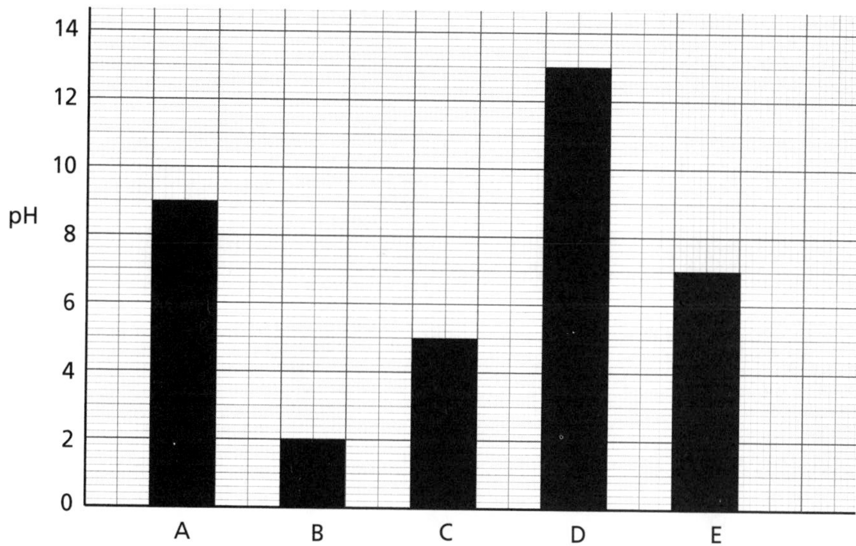

(a) Which of the above liquids

(i) is the most acidic? ☐ 4ai 1 mark

(ii) is the most alkaline? ☐ 4aii 1 mark

(iii) is neutral? ☐ 4aiii 1 mark

(b) What would happen to the pH of liquid D if liquid acid was added to it? Choose the correct statement by ticking a box.

(i) Its pH would stay the same ☐

(ii) Its pH would decrease ☐

(iii) Its pH would increase ☐

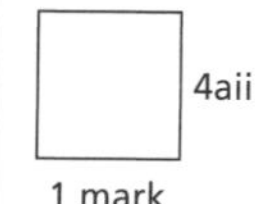
4b 1 mark

(c) What would happen to the pH of liquid C if liquid alkali was added to it? Choose the correct statement by ticking a box.

(i) Its pH would stay the same ☐

(ii) Its pH would decrease ☐

(iii) Its pH would increase ☐

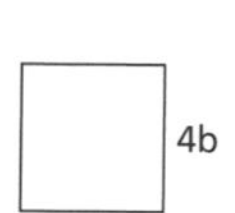
4c 1 mark

(d) Which of the above liquids is water?

____

4d 1 mark

Maximum 6 marks

5. The diagram below shows a tennis ball in mid-flight, just after it has been hit by a tennis racket.

A

B

(a) What force acts at A?

5a 1 mark

(b)(i) What force acts at B?

5bi 1 mark

(ii) What effect will this force eventually have on the ball?

5bii 1 mark

(c) Which of the following descriptions best describes the motion of the ball after it has been struck? Tick the correct one.

(i) The ball immediately accelerates then slows down gradually ☐

(ii) The ball continues to accelerate ☐

(iii) The ball starts to decelerate as soon as it leaves the racket ☐

(iv) The ball decelerates at first but then accelerates ☐

5c 1 mark

(d) Describe the motion of the ball if it had been struck by a spaceman in outer space.

5d 2 marks

Maximum 6 marks

6. Jamie is investigating how the strength of an electromagnet depends on the number of cells used. He is going to measure how many paper clips the electromagnet can pick up when the number of cells is changed. To begin with, he uses the following circuit.

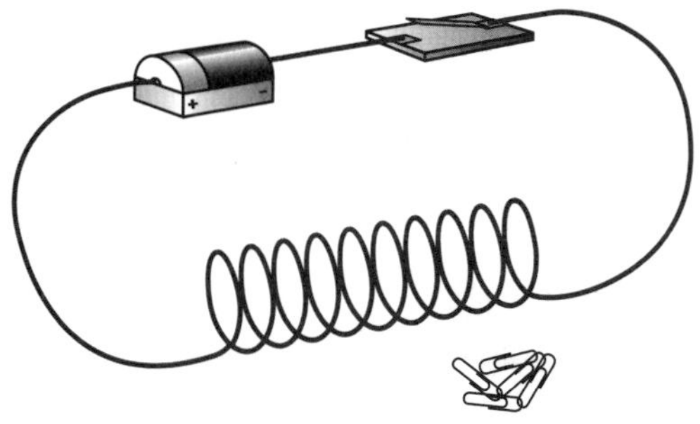

(a) What passes through the coil when the switch is closed?

____

6a
1 mark

(b) Give two factors that Jamie should keep the same in order to make the investigation fair.

1 ____

2 ____

6b
2 marks

(c) The table below shows his results.

Number of cells	1	2	3	4	5	6
Number of paper clips picked up	5	9	15	24	25	31

(i) What conclusion can Jamie draw from the results?

____

6ci
1 mark

(ii) Which one of his results looks wrong?

____

6cii
1 mark

(iii) What result would you expect in place of this wrong result?

____

6ciii
1 mark

Maximum 6 marks

7. Sophie was carrying out an experiment to investigate the reflection of light by a mirror. A ray of light was shone at a mirror at a known angle of incidence. The reflected ray was marked and the angle of reflection measured.

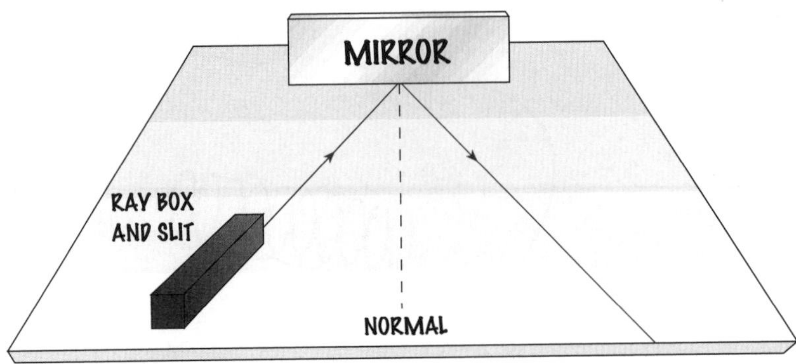

(a) Unfortunately, Sophie mislaid some of the results. Complete the table below to show the results you would expect her to have got.

Angle of incidence (°)	Angle of reflection (°)
15	
30	31
45	
60	59
70	

7a
3 marks

(b) What instrument would she have used to measure the different angles of incidence and angles of reflection?

____

7b
1 mark

(c) What conclusion can she draw from her investigation?

____

____

7c
1 mark

(d) What would happen to a ray of light if it was shone at a mirror along the normal?

____

7d
1 mark

Maximum 6 marks

8. (a) Look at the diagram of the skin cells (epithelial cells) below.

(i) What are the black structures labelled x?

____ 8ai

1 mark

(ii) What substance forms the 'body' of the cell, labelled y?

____ 8aii

1 mark

(iii) Explain how skin cells (epithelial cells) are well adapted to their function.

____

____ 8iii

2 marks

(b) Write down the names of the cells shown below.

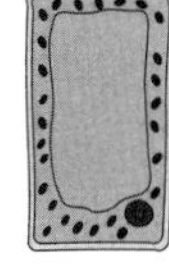 ________________________________

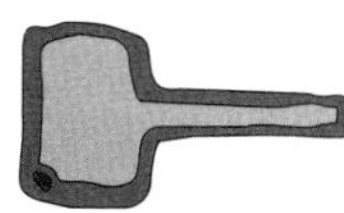 ________________________________

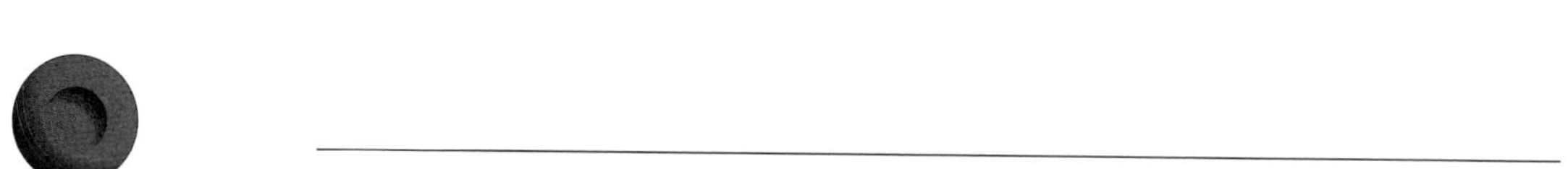

8b

2 marks

Maximum 6 marks

9.

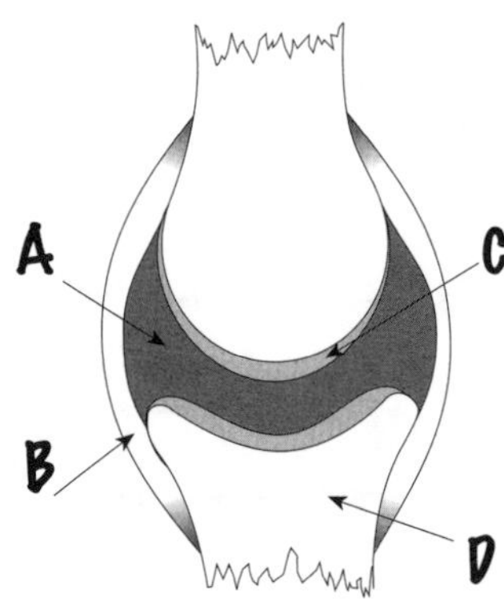

(a) The diagram above shows a knee joint. Name the structures shown in the joint.

Structure A ______________________

Structure B ______________________

Structure C ______________________

Structure D ______________________

9a 2 marks

X
Z
Y
X

(b)(i) What is the name given to the parts labelled X in the diagram above?

____

9bi 1 mark

(ii) Describe one important property of this structure.

____

9bii 1 mark

(iii) Which muscle, Y or Z, would you have to contract if you wished to lift your hand to your mouth?

____

9biii 1 mark

(iv) Which muscle, Y or Z, would you have to contract if you did a press-up?

____

9biv 1 mark

Maximum 6 marks

10. Scorpion European Leech Roman Snail Dor Beetle Honey Bee

Common Earthworm Common Mussel Lobster Woodlouse Garden Spider

(a) The diagrams above show invertebrate animals. Place them into the correct groups in the tables below. There are two animals in each group, and two have already been done for you.

Annelids		
Molluscs		Common Mussel
Crustaceans		
Arachnids		
Insects	Honey Bee	

10a 2 marks

(b) What is an invertebrate animal?

10b 1 mark

(c) Luke had jotted down some notes about the invertebrate animals he had seen in a nearby wood. Look at his descriptions below and try to identify the animal group to which they belong.

(i) The body was divided into three parts. There were three pairs of legs and two pairs of wings. The outside was hard and shiny and it had jointed legs.
The group the animal belongs to is...

10ci 1 mark

(ii) The body was divided into segments. There were bristles on the segments but no legs. I couldn't see any eyes.
The group the animal belongs to is...

10cii 1 mark

(iii) The body was divided into two parts. It had four pairs of legs, which were jointed, but there were no wings. The outside of the body was hard and shiny.
The group this animal belongs to is...

10ciii 1 mark

Maximum 6 marks

11.

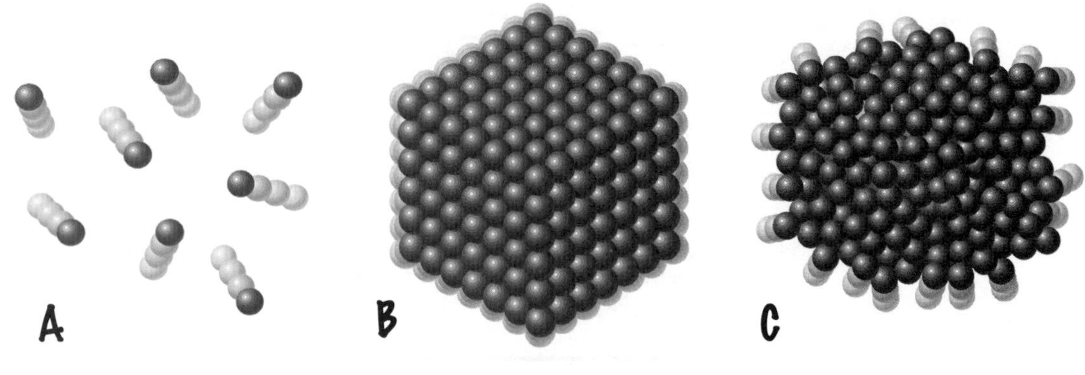

(a) Which one of the diagrams above would best represent a liquid?

11a
1 mark

(b) Which one of the diagrams above would best represent a gas?

11b
1 mark

(c) Which one of the diagrams above would best represent a solid?

11c
1 mark

(d) Sarah told Rebecca that liquids have particles that:

(i) are packed closely together
(ii) exert no pull force between them
(iii) move around in any direction.

Which one of these statements is wrong?

11d
1 mark

(e) What happens to the particles in a liquid as the temperature of the liquid rises?

11e
1 mark

(f) What happens to these particles if the temperature of the liquid reaches boiling point?

11f
1 mark

Maximum 6 marks

12. (a) There are five common methods of separating mixtures.

- Sieving
- Filtration
- Evaporation
- Distillation
- Chromatography

Decide which of these methods would be the best way of separating the mixtures below.

Sand and gravel ______________________

The different pigments in paint ______________________

Chalk and water ______________________

Sugar and water ______________________

Alcohol and water ______________________

Tea leaves and tea ______________________

12a

3 marks

(b)

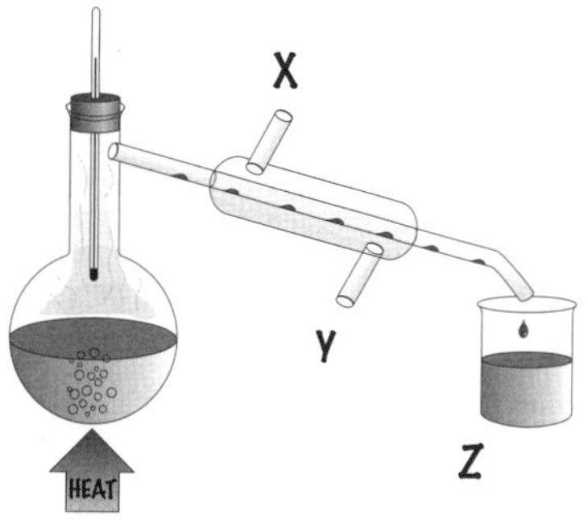

X

Y

Z

HEAT

The apparatus above was used to separate two liquids. Liquid A boils at 90°C while liquid B boils at 135°C.

(i) At which point, X or Y, should the cold water enter the condenser?

____

12bi

1 mark

(ii) Which of the liquids should end up in the beaker labelled Z?

____

12bii

1 mark

(iii) What would happen if the original mixture was heated to a temperature of 135°C?

____

____

12biii

1 mark

Maximum 6 marks

13. (a) Katie and Rachael performed a simple experiment to see what happened when a clean iron nail was placed into a beaker of copper sulphate solution. They recorded what happened by drawing the following diagrams:

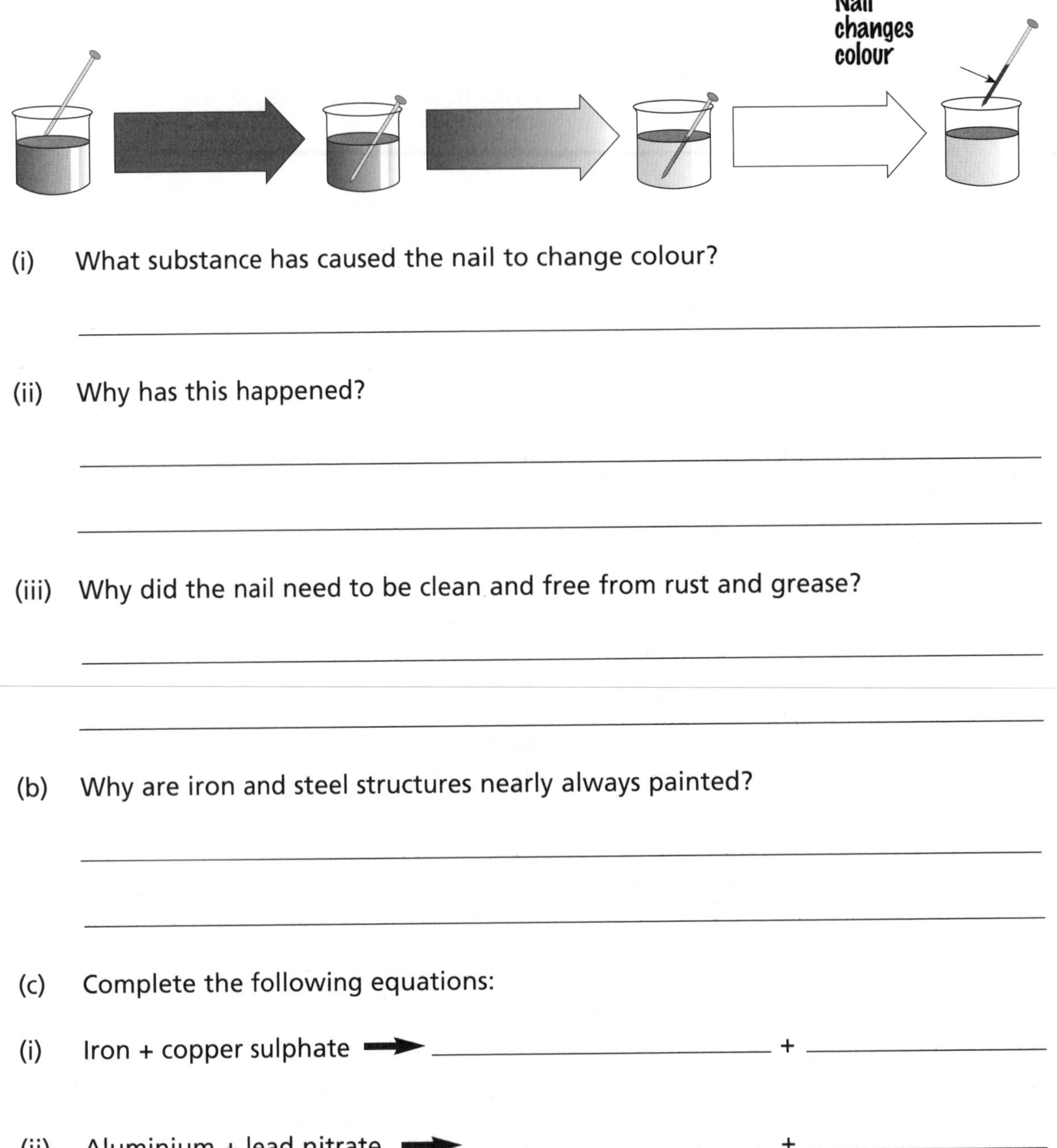

(i) What substance has caused the nail to change colour?

____

13ai 1 mark

(ii) Why has this happened?

____

____

13aii 1 mark

(iii) Why did the nail need to be clean and free from rust and grease?

____

____

13aiii 1 mark

(b) Why are iron and steel structures nearly always painted?

____

____

13b 1 mark

(c) Complete the following equations:

(i) Iron + copper sulphate ➞ ____________________ + ____________________

13ci 1 mark

(ii) Aluminium + lead nitrate ➞ ____________________ + ____________________

13cii 1 mark

Maximum 6 marks

14. (a) The following electrical devices all transfer electrical energy into other forms of energy.

What is the main form of energy transfer that takes place in each device?

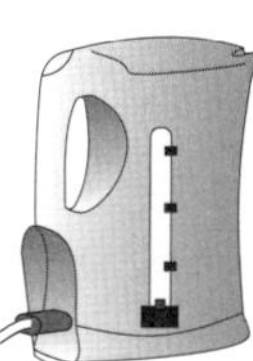  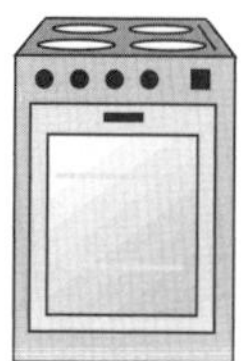 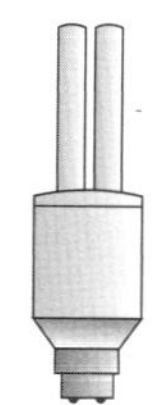

The electric kettle mainly transfers electrical energy into ____________

The electric drill mainly transfers electrical energy into ____________

The electric cooker mainly transfers electrical energy into ____________

The low energy light bulb mainly transfers electrical energy into ____________

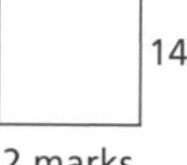
14a
2 marks

(b) Which of the circuits below transfers the most energy every second? ____________

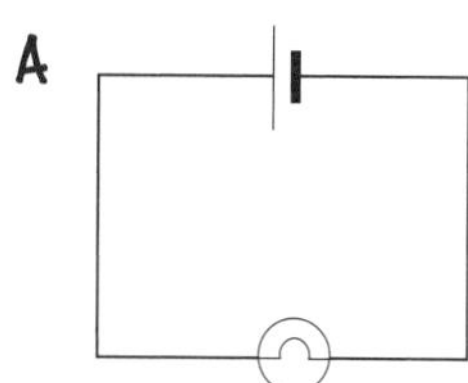

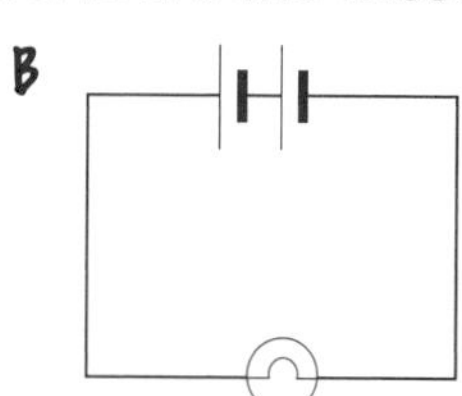

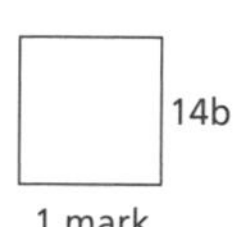
14b
1 mark

(c) On the circuit shown below, draw the position that a voltmeter would need to be placed in to measure the voltage across the lamp.

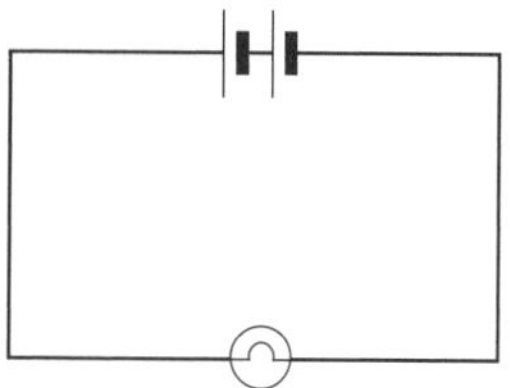

14c
1 mark

(d) For each of the following circuits, write down the value of the missing voltage.

(i)

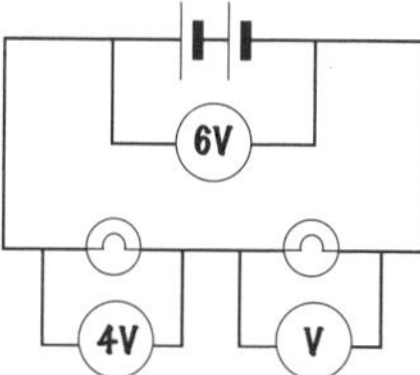

V= ____________ volts

14di
1 mark

(ii)

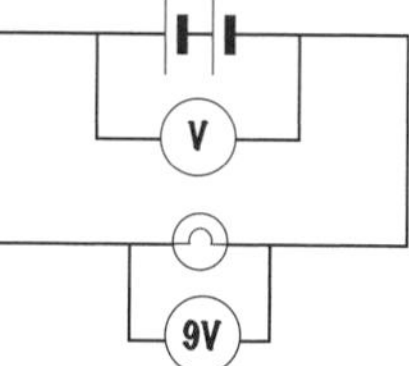

V = ____________ volts

14dii
1 mark

Maximum 6 marks

15. (a) Name a unit of pressure.

15a
1 mark

(b) Why are high-heeled shoes banned from certain types of floor?

15b
1 mark

(c) Write down the formula for pressure.

15c
1 mark

(d) With specific reference to pressure, why is it an advantage for camels to have big feet?

15d
1 mark

(e) Calculate the pressure exerted on the ground by each hoof if a horse has a weight of 5 000N and each hoof has an area of $125cm^2$.

15e
2 marks

Maximum 6 marks

Sc

KEY STAGE
3

TIER
3-6

Science test

Paper 2B

Please read this page carefully but do not open the booklet until you are told to start. Write your name and the name of your school in the spaces below.

First name ______________________________

Last name ______________________________

School name ______________________________

Remember

- The test is 1 hour long.
- You should have the following things on your desk: pen, pencil, rubber, ruler, protractor and calculator.
- The easier questions are at the beginning of the test.
- Try your best to answer all of the questions.
- The marks available for each question are shown below the mark boxes at the side of each question.
- Do not use rough paper. Write your answers and any working on the paper itself.
- Don't forget to check your work carefully.
- Ask your teacher if you are unsure about anything.

Total marks	

For marker's use only

Lonsdale

1. (a) Use the words below to complete the following sentences.

fat **carbohydrate** **protein**

1ai 1 mark

(i) Fish, meat, eggs and beans are sources of ______________________ .

1aii 1 mark

(ii) Potatoes, bread and cereals are sources of ______________________ .

1aiii 1 mark

(iii) Milk, butter and cheese are sources of ______________________ .

(b) Look at the table. It shows the nutritional values for two different types of potato crisps.

	100g of potato crisp A	100g of potato crisp B
Energy	1900kJ	2200kJ
Protein	8g	6g
Carbohydrate	58g	52g
Fat	22g	34g
Fibre	4.5g	4g

(i) Which potato crisp contains the most energy?

1bi 1 mark

____

(ii) Which potato crisp is the healthier option? Give two reasons why this is.

____

____

1bii 2 marks

____

Maximum 6 marks

2. (a) Look at the animals below.

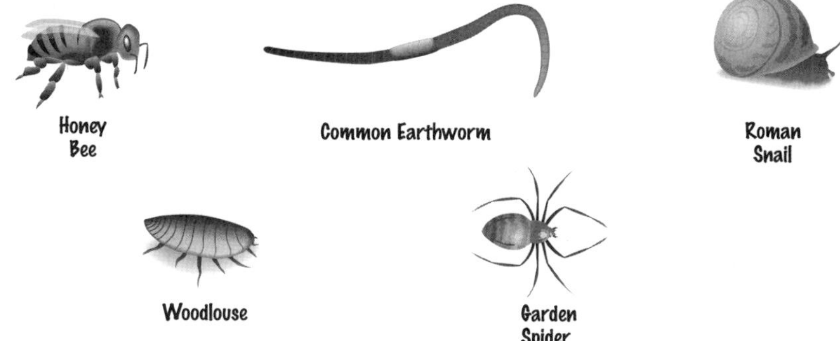

(i) Which of these animals would have a body made up of three segments?

____

2ai 1 marks

(ii) Which of these animals would have wings?

____

2aii 1 mark

(iii) Which two of these animals need moisture in order to breathe?

1 ______________________________

2 ______________________________

2aiii 2 marks

(b) Look at the three animals below.

(i) What collective name is given to these three animals?

____

2bi 1 mark

(ii) What do these creatures have that those in part (a) do not have?

____

2bii 1 mark

Maximum 6 marks

3. The graph below shows how the temperature of a material being heated changes against time. To begin with, the material was in a solid state.

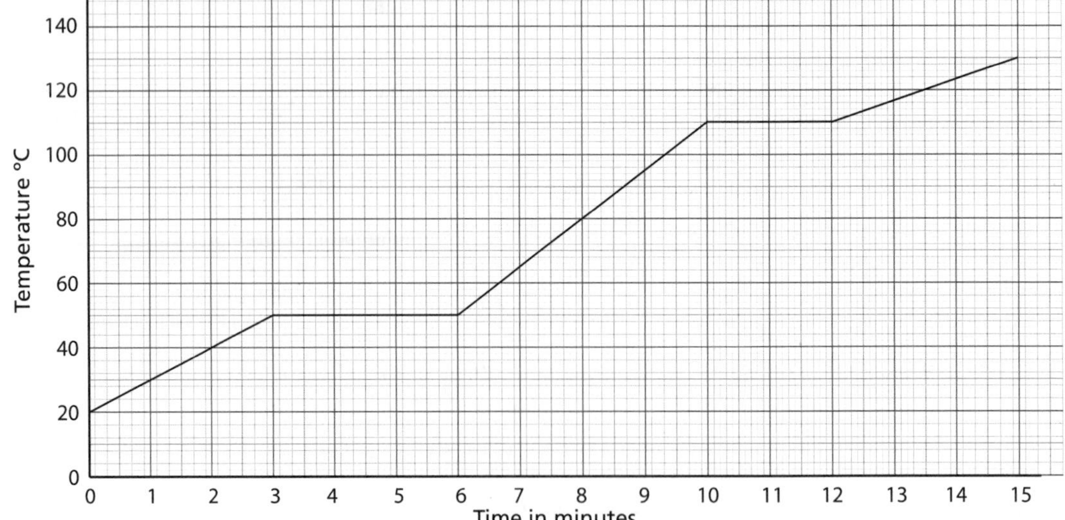

(a) Write down the state that the material was in at the following temperatures.

3a
1 mark

(i) 90°C ______________________

3aii
1 mark

(ii) 40°C ______________________

3aiii
1 mark

(iii) 120°C ______________________

3bi
1 mark

(b)(i) What is the melting point of this material?

____

3bii
1 mark

(ii) What is the boiling point of this material?

____

3c
1 mark

(c) The mass of the material to begin with was 120 grams. What would be the mass of the material after 8 minutes?

____

Maximum 6 marks

4. (a) Which of the following are pollutant gases produced when fossil fuels are burned by industry and car engines? Tick the boxes next to the three correct answers.

oxygen	☐	hydrogen	☐
carbon dioxide	☐	sulphur dioxide	☐
nitrogen	☐	oxides of nitrogen	☐

4ai
3 marks

(b) These gases then dissolve in rain water to produce acid rain. Ann carried out a demonstration to show what happens when acid rain comes into contact with limestone.

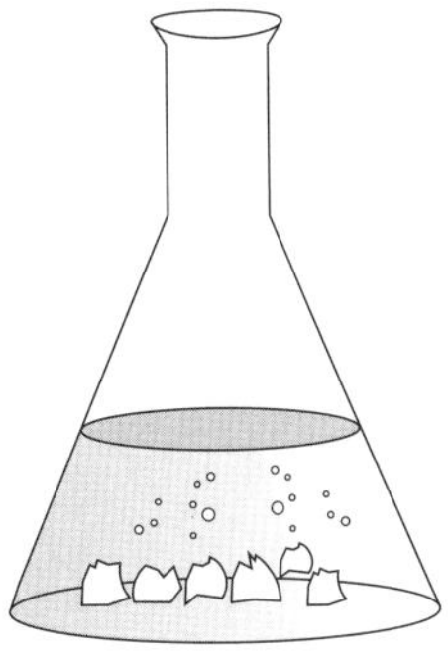

(i) How can Ann tell that a reaction is taking place?

____

4bi
1 mark

(ii) Many stone buildings and structures are made of limestone. What physical effect does acid rain have on them over a long period of time?

____

4bii
1 mark

(c) Why is it that pollutant gases produced by one country may lead to acid rain falling in a different country?

____

4c
1 mark

Maximum 6 marks

5. (a) Heat energy is transferred from a hotter place to a cooler place by four different methods. Draw lines to link each method of transfer to its definition.

Conduction	Transfer of heat energy by waves
Convection	Transfer of heat energy due to the loss of particles from the surface of liquids
Radiation	Transfer of heat energy through a substance without any movement of the substance itself
Evaporation	Transfer of heat energy through the movement of the particles themselves

5a

4 marks

(b) Paula carried out a simple experiment. She trapped an ice cube at the bottom of a test tube of water using a piece of gauze. She then heated the test tube near the top until the water boiled. She found that the ice cube remained unmelted even though the water near the top carried on boiling.

Tick the box next to the statement which explains why the ice did not melt.

(i) The wire gauze is a poor conductor of heat energy ☐

(ii) The water is a good conductor of heat energy ☐

(iii) The water is a poor conductor of heat energy ☐

5b

1 mark

(c) Paula noticed that during the winter her dad always wore a stringed vest underneath his shirt. He told her that it traps air between his skin and his shirt which keeps him warm. Is air a good conductor or a bad conductor of heat energy?

____

5c

1 mark

Maximum 6 marks

6. (a) Complete the sentences below by filling in the blanks.

The law of reflection states that the angle of ______________________ is equal to the angle of __________________ .

6a 2 marks

(b) Complete the following diagrams by drawing the reflected rays.

(i)

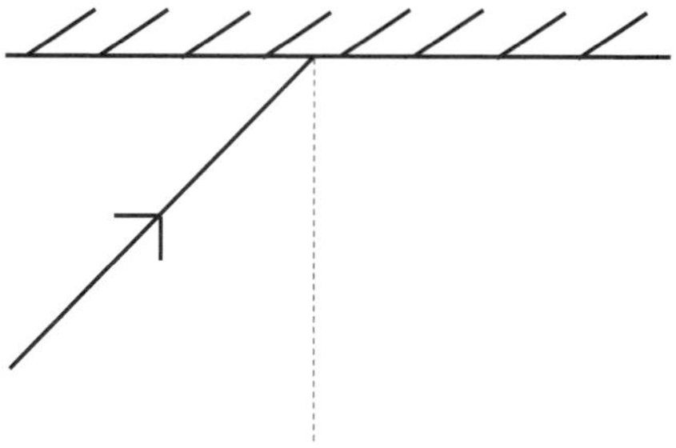

6bi 1 mark

(ii)

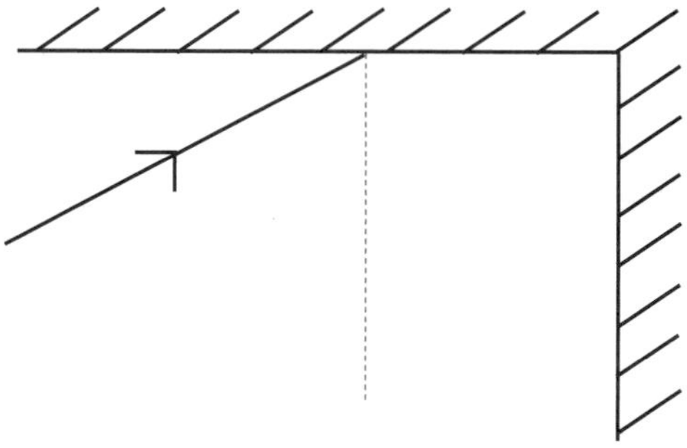

6bii 1 mark

(iii)

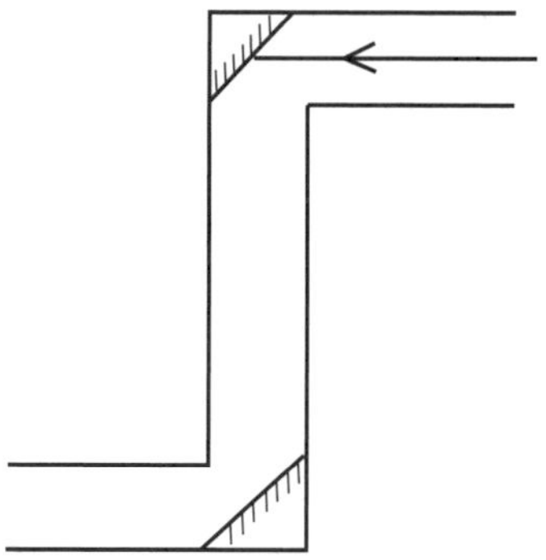

6biii 1 mark

(c) What use could the arrangement in (b) (iii) be put to?

____

6c 1 mark

Maximum 6 marks

7. The table below gives the useful energy output per second for every 100 Joules of energy input per second for five energy transfer mechanisms.

Energy transfer mechanism	Useful energy output per second (J/s)
Tungsten filament light bulb	20
Low energy light bulb	80
Electric kettle	90
Electric drill	60
Fossil fuel power station	30

(a) Which of the above mechanisms is the most useful at transferring energy?

7a
1 mark

(b) Which of the above mechanisms is the least useful at transferring energy?

7b
1 mark

(c) Complete the following bar chart to show the information in the table above.

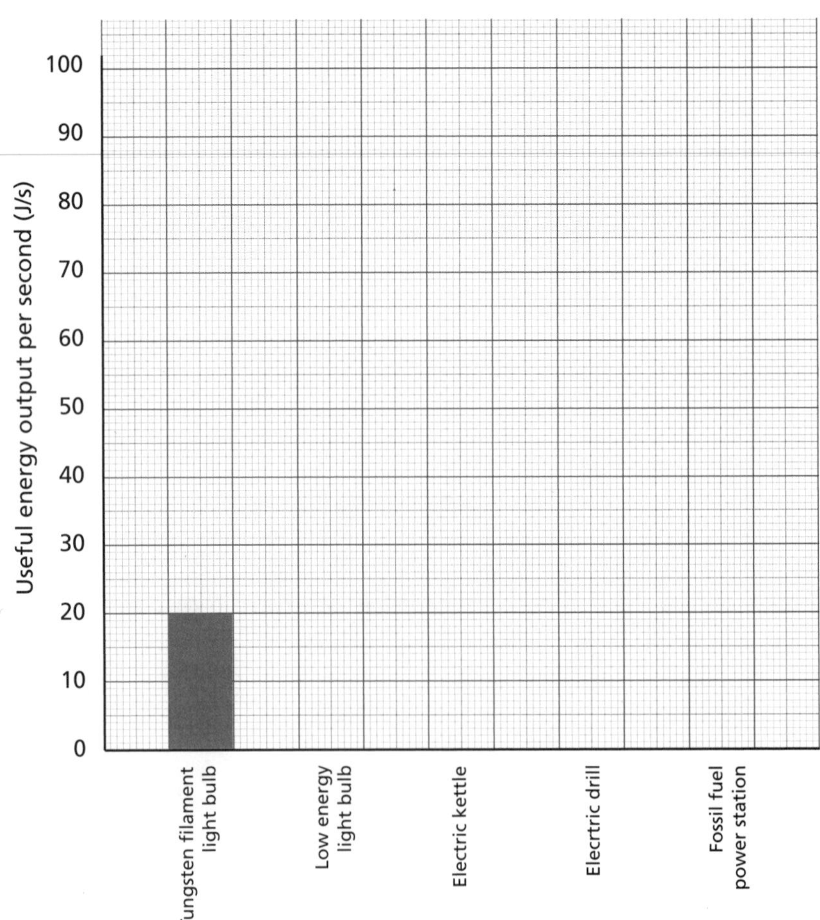

7c
4 marks

Maximum 6 marks

8. The diagram below shows a plant cell.

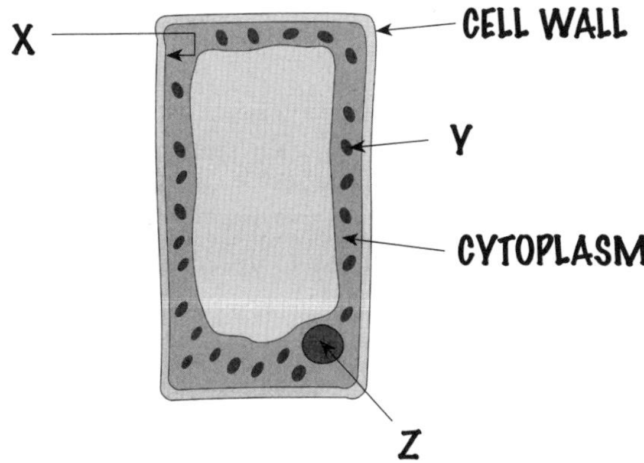

(a) Name the parts that are labelled X, Y and Z on the diagram.

(i) X ____________________ 8ai 1 mark

(ii) Y ____________________ 8aii 1 mark

(iii) Z ____________________ 8aiii 1 mark

(b) Which part of the plant cell controls what enters and leaves the cell?

____________________ 8b 1 mark

(c) Which part of the plant cell contains the genetic material?

____________________ 8c 1 mark

(d) In which part of the plant cell does photosynthesis take place?

____________________ 8d 1 mark

Maximum 6 marks

9. Amy and Jacques planted some cress seeds in four different trays so that each tray of seeds had different growing conditions.

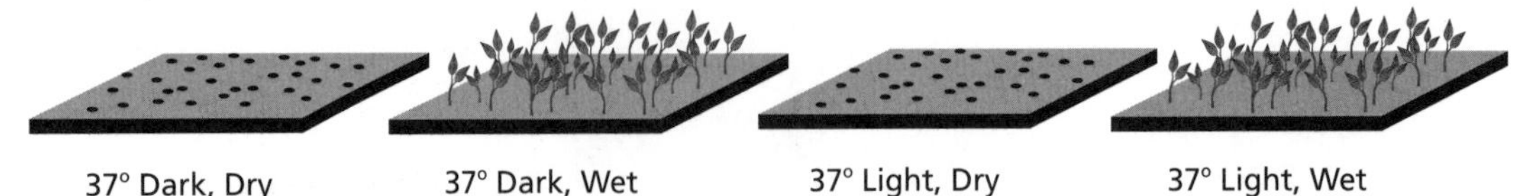

(a) Which factor would seem to be necessary for the germination of the seeds?

____

9a
1 mark

(b) Which factor is it impossible to comment on?

____

9b
1 mark

(c) How could you perform a fair investigation to discover whether this factor has any effect?

____

____

____

____

____

9c
4 marks

Maximum 6 marks

10. In an investigation into how the digestive system works, a visking tubing 'bag' was filled with a mixture of starch solution and sugar solution, and then sealed.

The bag was then placed in a boiling tube containing pure water and was allowed to stand for one hour. After this time had passed, a sample was taken from the water in the boiling tube and tested for both sugar and starch solutions.

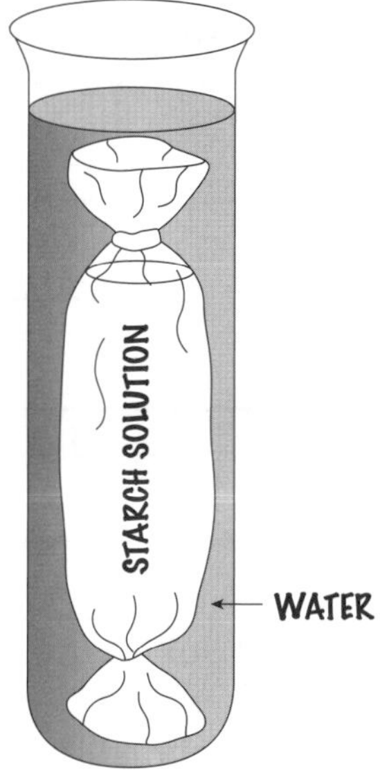

(a) What test would be used to test for starch solution?

____ 10a 1 mark

(b) What test would be used to test for sugar solution?

____ 10b 1 mark

(c)(i) What would you expect to find in the water of the boiling tube after one hour?

____ 10ci 1 mark

(ii) Explain your answer to part (i)

____

____ 10cii 2 marks

(d) Starch is converted to sugar in the human digestive system. What is the name of the substance which causes this?

____ 10d 1 mark

Maximum 6 marks

11. (a) Draw lines from the two central boxes below to match up metal elements and non-metal elements to their characteristics. Draw four lines only.

Not shiny, half are gases	**Metal elements**	Shiny solid at room temperature
Good conductors of heat and electricity	**Non metal elements**	Poor conductors of heat and electricity

11a
4 marks

(b) Look at the following list. Underline two substances which are elements.

carbon water brass ice oxygen carbon dioxide plastic

11b
1 mark

(c) Look at the following list. Underline two substances which are metal elements.

sulphur helium tin nitrogen calcium chlorine hydrogen

11c
1 mark

Maximum 6 marks

12. In an experiment to compare the amount of energy in different foods, the following apparatus was used.

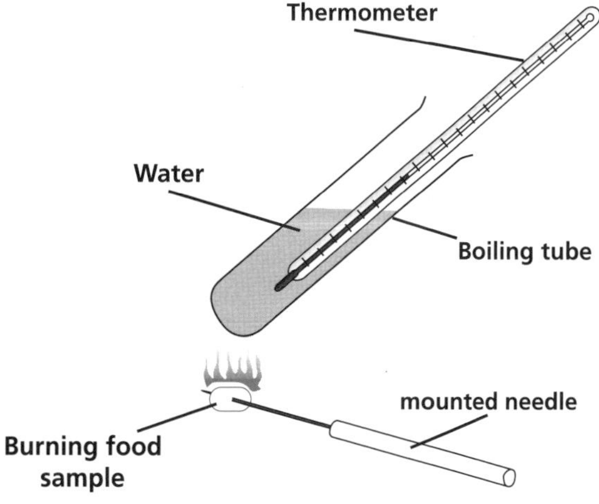

(a) In order to make a fair comparison between the energy in a peanut and the energy in a piece of bread, which three variables would need to be controlled?

1 ______________________________

2 ______________________________

3 ______________________________

12a
3 marks

(b) What would have to be measured in order to make the comparison?

____

12b
1 mark

(c) Why would this apparatus provide only a rough comparison between the two food types?

____

12c
1 mark

(d) In this investigation, peanuts were found to contain more energy than bread. Explain the reason for this.

____

____

12d
1 mark

Maximum 6 marks

13. The eight metals below have been placed in order of their reactivity.

potassium sodium calcium magnesium aluminium zinc iron copper

most reactive ⟷ least reactive

(a) Predict what will happen when the following occur:

(i) A piece of iron is placed in copper sulphate solution.

13ai
1 mark

(ii) A piece of copper is placed in magnesium nitrate solution.

13aii
1 mark

(iii) A mixture of aluminium powder and iron oxide is heated.

13aiii
1 mark

(iv) A piece of magnesium is placed in aluminium sulphate solution.

13aiv
1 mark

(b) Gold is lower than copper in the reactivity series. Explain why gold is found in pure form.

13b
1 mark

(c) When a piece of sodium is dropped into water it produces hydrogen quickly as it whizzes about, and it also gets very hot. Predict what would happen if potassium was placed in water.

13c
1 mark

Maximum 6 marks

14. (a) Sonia and Elaine set up the circuit below and experimented with the switches to see the effect on the lamps.

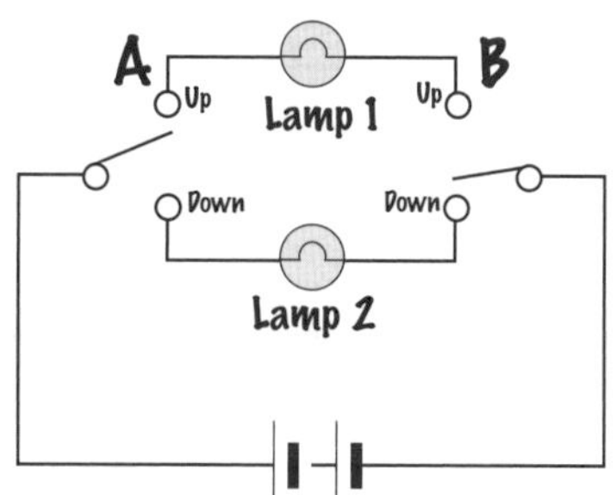

Complete the table below to show their findings.

SWITCH A	SWITCH B	LAMP 1 (ON or OFF)	LAMP 2 (ON or OFF)
UP	DOWN		
UP	UP		
DOWN	UP		
DOWN	DOWN		

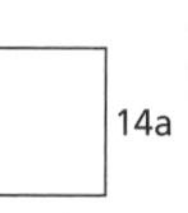

14a

4 marks

(b) Sonia and Elaine then set up the circuits below.

(i)

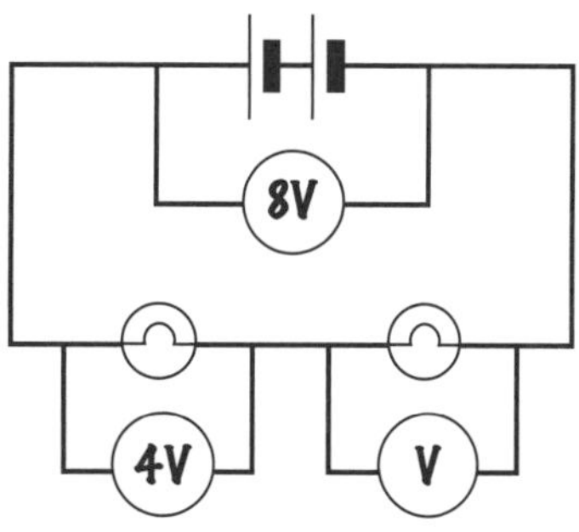

What reading would you expect to see on the voltmeter V?

____

14bi

1 mark

(ii)

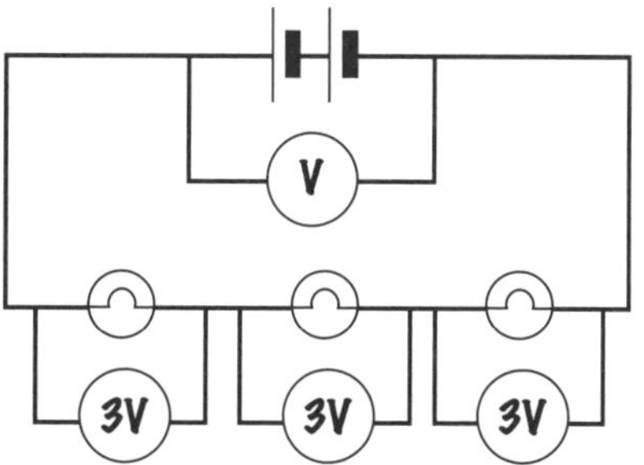

What reading would you expect to see on the voltmeter V?

____

14bii

1 mark

Maximum 6 marks

15. (a) Amir went on a cycling holiday. The holiday lasted for 4 days. Complete the table below showing his daily progress.

Day	Distance travelled (km)	Time taken (hours)	Average speed
1	60	5	
2		6	15
3	70		14
4		7	16

15a
4 marks

(b) What unit is his average speed measured in?

____

15b
1 mark

(c) When Amir applies his brakes, what force slows the bike down?

____

15c
1 mark

Maximum 6 marks

Sc

KEY STAGE
3

TIER
3-6

Science test

Paper 1C

Please read this page carefully but do not open the booklet until you are told to start. Write your name and the name of your school in the spaces below.

First name ______________________________

Last name ______________________________

School name ______________________________

Remember

- The test is 1 hour long.
- You should have the following things on your desk: pen, pencil, rubber, ruler, protractor and calculator.
- The easier questions are at the beginning of the test.
- Try your best to answer all of the questions.
- The marks available for each question are shown below the mark boxes at the side of each question.
- Do not use rough paper. Write your answers and any working on the paper itself.
- Don't forget to check your work carefully.
- Ask your teacher if you are unsure about anything.

Total marks	

For marker's use only

Lonsdale

1. The diagrams below show some specialised cells

A — A SPERM CELL
B — A RED BLOOD CELL
C — CILIATED EPITHELIAL CELLS
D — A ROOT HAIR CELL

(a)(i) Which one of these is a plant cell?

1ai
1 mark

____

(ii) Name two features that the plant cell would have which animal cells would not have.

1 ______________________________

2 ______________________________

1aii
1 mark

(b)(i) How are ciliated epithelial cells suited to the job they do?

1bi
1 mark

____

(ii) Give an example of where they might be found.

1bii
1 mark

____

(c)(i) In which part of the body are sperm cells produced?

1ci
1 mark

____

(ii) What is the name of the process in which a sperm fuses with an egg? Tick the correct box.

Implantation	☐	Ovulation	☐
Fertilisation	☐	Menstruation	☐

1cii
1 mark

Maximum 6 marks

2. The diagram below shows the respiratory system.

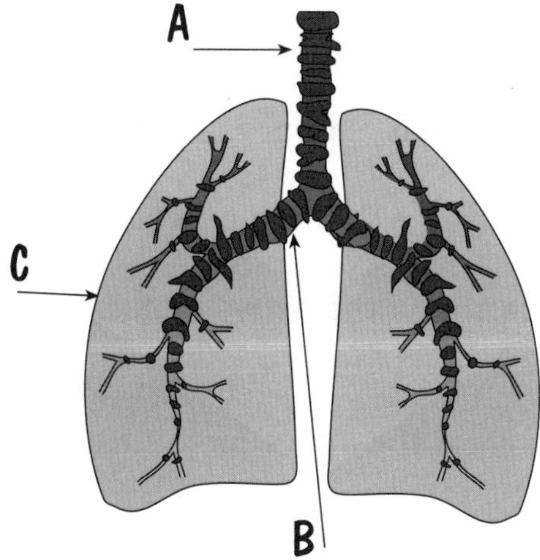

(a) Write down the names of the parts labelled in the diagram above.

(i) A is ______________________________ 2ai 1 mark

(ii) B is ______________________________ 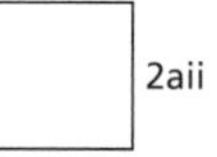 2aii 1 mark

(iii) C is ______________________________  2aiii 1 mark

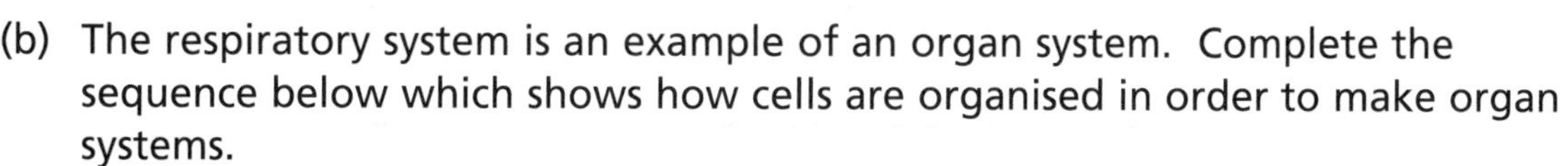

(b) The respiratory system is an example of an organ system. Complete the sequence below which shows how cells are organised in order to make organ systems.

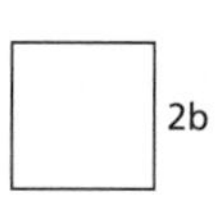 2b 1 mark

(c) Name two other organ systems

1 ______________________________

2 ______________________________

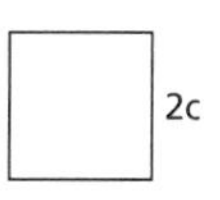 2c 2 marks

Maximum 6 marks

3. A displacement reaction is one in which a more reactive metal displaces a less reactive metal from a compound. Use the statements below to list the following metals in order of reactivity, with the most reactive at the top.

zinc **silver** **calcium** **iron** **aluminium** **lead**

Iron will displace lead from a solution of lead nitrate.

Silver will not displace any of the above metals from solutions of their compounds.

Calcium will displace all of the above metals from solutions of their compounds.

Zinc will displace iron from a solution of iron chloride but will not displace aluminium from a solution of aluminium chloride.

	MOST REACTIVE
	LEAST REACTIVE

3

6 marks

Maximum 6 marks

4. (a) Below are descriptions of the states of a particular substance. For each description write down in the box next to it whether the substance is in a solid, liquid or gas state.

(i) The substance can flow but its volume stays the same

4ai 1 mark

(ii) The substance can flow and can be compressed easily

4aii 1 mark

(iii) The substance cannot be compressed and it takes the shape of the bottom of a container

4aiii 1 mark

(iv) The volume of the substance stays the same and it does not flow

4aiv 1 mark

(b) Frances leaves some ice in a beaker. When she comes back an hour later she notices that the ice has melted into water. Tick the two statements that are correct.

(i) The mass of the water in the beaker is greater than the mass of the ice in the beaker

(ii) The melting of ice into water is an example of a chemical change

(iii) The mass of the water in the beaker is the same as the mass of the ice in the beaker

(iv) The melting of ice into water is an example of a physical change

(v) The mass of the water in the beaker is less than the mass of the ice that was in the beaker

4b 2 marks

Maximum 6 marks

5. (a) Here are ten energy resources.

food **coal** **tidal** **wind** **waves**
solar **gas** **oil** **biomass** **running water**

Complete the table below by writing each energy resource in the correct column.

Non-renewable	Renewable

5a
4 marks

(b) What is the original source of most energy resources? Tick the correct box.

Moon ☐

Sun ☐

Mars ☐

5b
1 mark

(c) A battery is a store of chemical energy. What form of energy is it transferred into in a complete circuit? Tick the correct box.

Kinetic ☐

Light ☐

Electrical ☐

5c
1 mark

Maximum 6 marks

6. (a) The diagrams below show the outlines of Bill's foot and of Derek's foot. Both are drawn on $1cm^2$ paper.

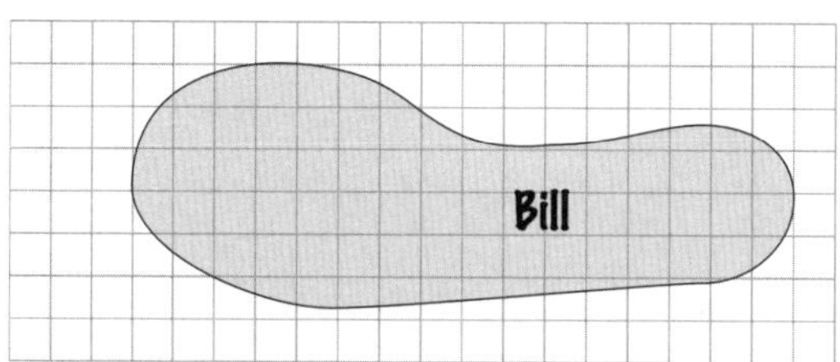

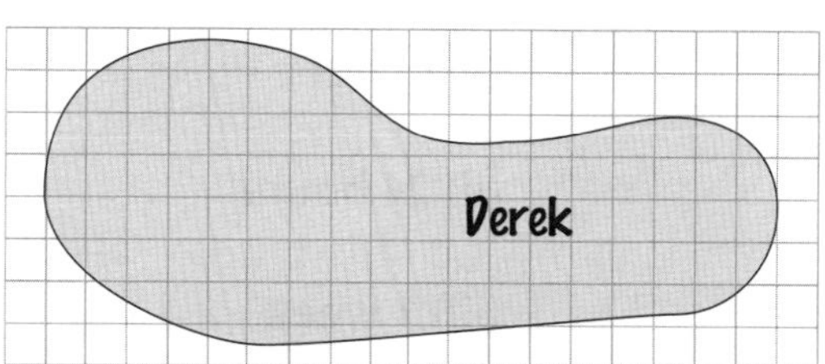

(i) Bill and Derek each weigh 400N. Who would exert the greatest pressure on the ground if they each stood on one foot?

____ 6ai 1 mark

(ii) Explain your answer to part (i).

____ 6aii 2 marks

(b) The amount of pressure exerted on a surface has some important practical applications in various situations. For each of the following examples, state whether the pressure exerted is **large** or **small.**

Using a sharp knife to cut through food	
Wearing stiletto shoes on a wooden floor	
Wearing snowshoes on snow	
Tractors having large tyres	
Football boots having studs	
Lorries having as many as eight wheels on their trailers	

6b 3 marks

Maximum 6 marks

7. (a) How long does it take for the Earth to complete one rotation? Tick the correct box.

(i) 1 hour ☐

(ii) 24 hours ☐

(iii) 1 week ☐

7a
1 mark

(b) Which of the following statements about summertime are correct? Tick two correct boxes.

(i) The Earth is tilted away from the Sun ☐

(ii) The Sun appears to be higher in the sky ☐

(iii) Night-time is longer than the daytime ☐

(iv) Daytime is longer than the night-time ☐

7b
2 marks

(c) Which of the following statements are correct about wintertime? Tick two correct boxes.

(i) The Earth is tilted away from the Sun ☐

(ii) The Earth is tilted towards the Sun ☐

(iii) The Sun appears to be lower in the sky ☐

(iv) Daytime is longer than night-time ☐

7c
2 marks

(d) During night-time the stars appear to move in curved paths across the sky. Tick the box next to the statement that is correct.

(i) The Sun is spinning around ☐

(ii) The Earth is spinning around ☐

7d
1 mark

8. (a) Look at the following set of data.

NUMBER OF CIGARETTES SMOKED PER DAY	10	20	30	40	50
INCREASED RISK OF DYING OF LUNG CANCER	x10	x18	x25	x33	x40

What can you say about how smoking can affect your chances of dying of lung cancer?

____

____

8a 1 mark

(b) Now look at this set of data.

YEAR	1920	1930	1940	1950	1960
NUMBER OF DEATHS PER 100,000 DUE TO LUNG CANCER	10	35	50	100	180

What conclusion can you draw from this data?

____

____

8b 1 mark

(c) Read the following sentences about smoking and fill in the blanks using the words below.

nicotine **carbon monoxide** **air sacs (alveoli)** **cilia**

Heart rate and blood pressure are increased by ________________ which is an addictive substance in cigarette smoke.

Constant coughing due to a build up of mucus damages the ________________. This can result in an illness called emphysema.

The tar causes mucus to build up and this stops the ________________ from 'beating'.

________________ from smoke prevents oxygen from being absorbed by the blood since it combines more easily with the blood.

8c 4 marks

Maximum 6 marks

9. The diagram below shows the digestive system.

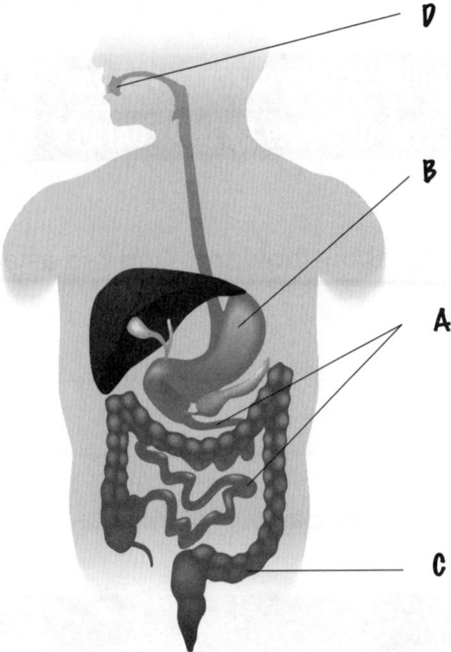

(a) What is the name given to part A ?

9a
1 mark

(b) What is the name given to part B?

9b
1 mark

(c) What is the name given to part C?

9c
1 mark

(d) What is the name given to part D?

9d
1 mark

After a meal the food you have eaten passes slowly through the digestive system where various things happen to it.

(e) In which part of the digestive system are all the nutrients from the food absorbed into the bloodstream?

9e
1 mark

(f) In which part of the digestive system is water reabsorbed into the body?

9f
1 mark

Maximum 6 marks

10. Yasmin investigated the organisms which lived in her local wood and produced the following simple food web.

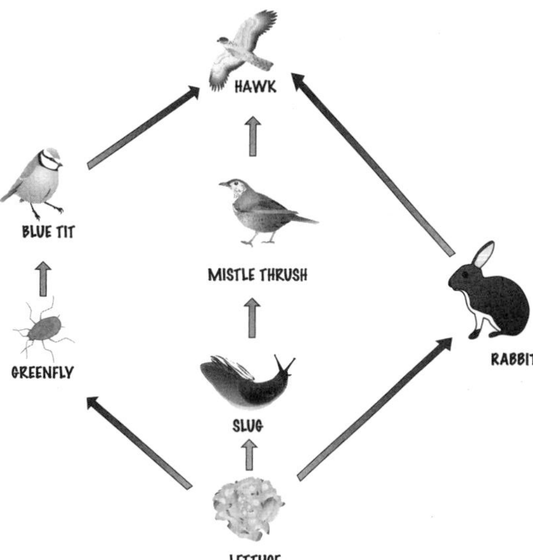

(a) Write down an example of a food chain from this food web in the spaces below.

__________ → __________ → __________ → __________

10a
1 mark

(b) Write down the name of one carnivore from the food web.

____

10b
1 mark

(c) Write down the name of two herbivores from the food web.

____

10c
2 marks

(d) Explain what would happen to the number of thrushes eaten by hawks if the blue tits died out.

____

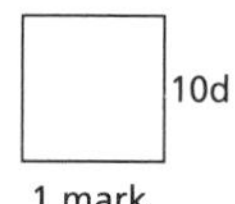
10d
1 mark

(e) What is the original source of energy for all the seven organisms in the food web?

____

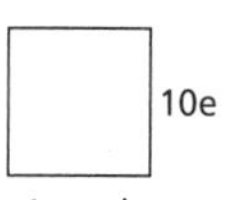
10e
1 mark

Maximum 6 marks

11. Grace and James performed an experiment to see how easily salt dissolved in water. They used water at different temperatures which was placed into glass beakers. The salt was added using a small spoon and was stirred until it dissolved. The number of spoonfuls dissolved in each beaker was noted.

Temperature of water (°C)	Number of spoonfuls of salt which dissolved
10	3
20	5
30	9

(a) What conclusion can be drawn by Grace and James about how the solubility of salt changes as the temperature of the water increases?

____

____

11a

1 mark

(b) What else, apart from the amount of stirring, would need to be kept the same in order for this to be a fair test?

____

____

11b

1 mark

(c) Grace and James then experimented with three other types of solvent. The ones they chose were alcohol, petrol and turpentine. Name two things which they would have to keep the same in order for this to be a fair test.

____

____

11c

2 marks

(d) What factor would you expect Grace and James to measure in this second investigation? And what units should they use?

____

____

11d

2 marks

Maximum 6 marks

12. Some Year 9 pupils used the equipment below to investigate how increasing the amount of metal in a chemical reaction with acid affected the amount of gas given off. They continued to add acid until all the metal had disappeared. Their results are shown below.

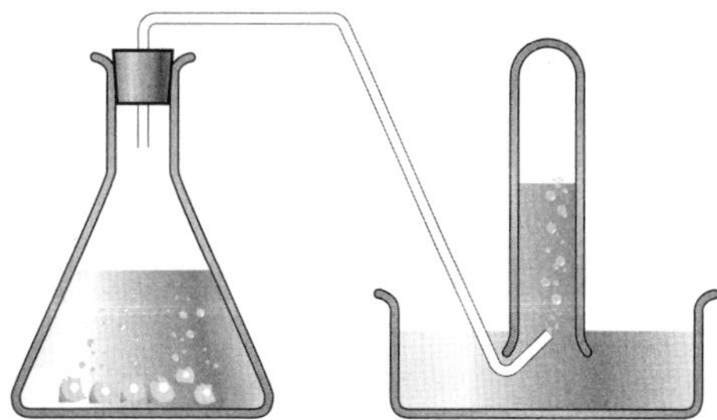

Mass of metal (g)	0.5	1.0	1.5	2.0	2.5	3.0	3.5	4.0
Volume of gas (cm^3)	400	900	1300	1800	2000	2700	3200	3700

(a) Suggest one thing you might observe which would tell you that the acid and the metal were taking part in a chemical reaction.

____

12a 1 mark

(b) If the acid was hydrochloric and the metal was zinc, which gas would be formed?

____

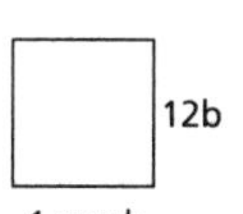

12b 1 mark

(c) Plot the results onto the graph paper below ensuring that the points are plotted accurately. Draw a line of best fit.

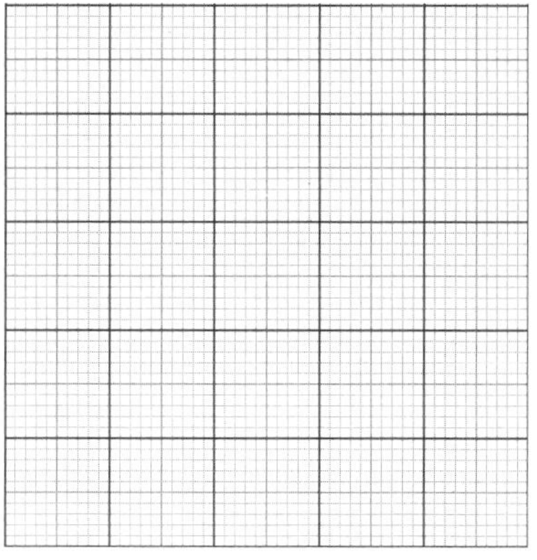

12c 2 marks

(d) What conclusion can you draw from these results?

____

____

12d 1 mark

(e) What can you say about the accuracy of these results?

____

12e 1 mark

Maximum 6 marks

13a
1 mark

13. (a) Put a circle around the elements in this list.

Oxygen Salt Iron Wood Water Sodium Carbon dioxide Gold

(b) Write down the names of two gases from the list above.

1 ____________________

2 ____________________

13b
1 mark

(c) Write down the names of two metals from the list above.

1 ____________________

2 ____________________

13c
1 mark

(d) Write down the name of a compound which contains only hydrogen and oxygen.

____

13d
1 mark

Look at the following list of substances.

Magnesium Sulphur Helium Sodium chloride Oxygen

(e) Write down the name of a substance from this list, which is a shiny solid at room temperature and is also a good conductor of heat and electricity.

____

13e
1 mark

(f) Write down the name of an inert gas from this list, which is lighter than air.

____

13f
1 mark

Maximum 6 marks

Lonsdale

14. (a) An aeroplane travelling from London to Rome covers 200km in 15min.

(i) What was the average speed of the aeroplane? Please include the unit.

14ai

1 mark

(ii) What can you say about how the forward force on the aeroplane compares with the backward force when it is travelling at a constant speed?

14aii

1 mark

(b) Halfway through the journey the pilot experiences engine problems and has to reduce the amount of thrust produced by them.

(i) As he reduces the thrust how does the forward force now compare with the backward force?

14bi

1 mark

(ii) What immediate effect will this have on the speed of the aeroplane?

14bii

1 mark

(c) The pilot finds that he can't solve the problem and must continue in this way for the rest of the trip.

(i) Assuming the thrust stays at the same reduced level and external conditions remain the same, what can you say about the new speed of the aeroplane in addition to what you have said in answer to the previous question.

14ci

1 mark

(ii) How can you explain this in terms of the forward and backward forces on the aeroplane?

14cii

1 mark

Maximum 6 marks

15. A group of students is investigating how the strength of an electromagnet depends on the number of coils of wire it consists of. They are going to count the number of paper clips the different sized electromagnets can pick up.

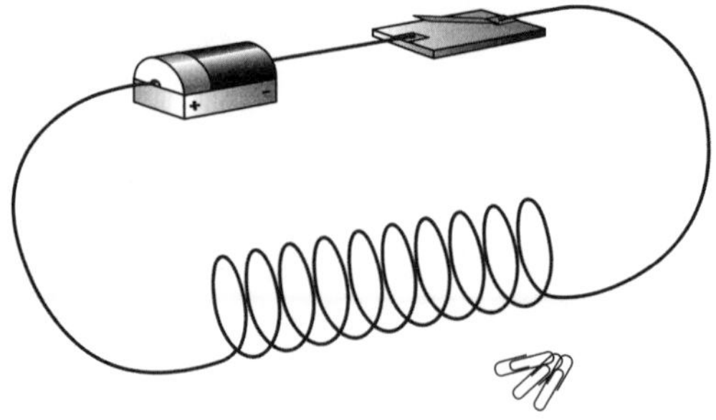

(a) Name one factor which must be kept the same in order to make this a fair test.

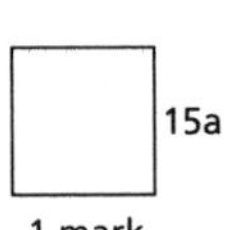
15a
1 mark

(b) The students' results are shown below. They carried out each experiment three times for each electromagnet. Complete the table by working out the average results.

	No. of paperclips picked up			
Coils of wire	**Expt 1**	**Expt 2**	**Expt 3**	**Average**
5	4	4	4	
10	9	8	7	
15	13	12	11	
20	18	16	17	
25	21	20	22	
30	24	23	25	

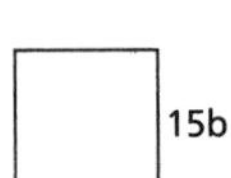
15b
2 marks

(c) Plot these results on the graph paper below and draw a line of best fit.

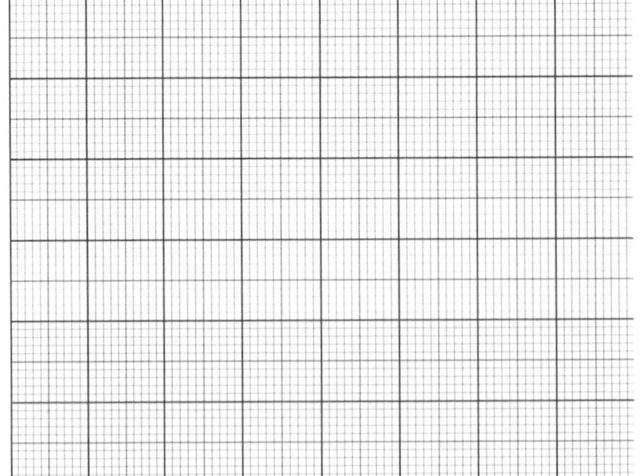

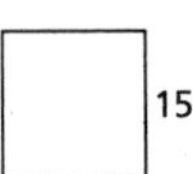
15c
2 marks

(d) What conclusion can the group draw from these results?

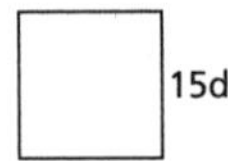
15d
1 mark

Maximum 6 marks

Sc

KEY STAGE
3

TIER
3-6

Science test

Paper 2C

Please read this page carefully but do not open the booklet until you are told to start. Write your name and the name of your school in the spaces below.

First name ____________________

Last name ____________________

School name ____________________

Remember

- The test is 1 hour long.
- You should have the following things on your desk: pen, pencil, rubber, ruler, protractor and calculator.
- The easier questions are at the beginning of the test.
- Try your best to answer all of the questions.
- The marks available for each question are shown below the mark boxes at the side of each question.
- Do not use rough paper. Write your answers and any working on the paper itself.
- Don't forget to check your work carefully.
- Ask your teacher if you are unsure about anything.

Total marks	

For marker's use only

Lonsdale

1. The graph below shows the number of males per 1000 of the population who drink more than 30 units of alcohol per week.

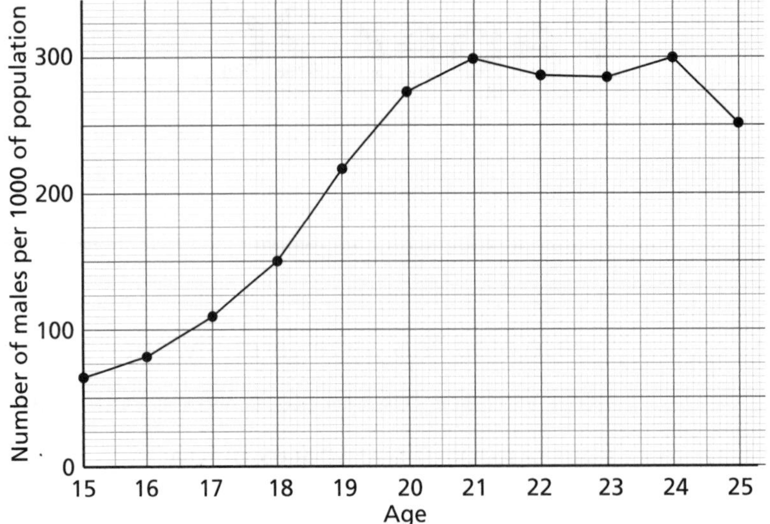

(a)(i) How many males aged 21 drink more than 30 units of alcohol per week?

1ai
1 mark

____

(ii) Express your answer to (i) above as a percentage

1aii
1 mark

____

(b) Name two parts of the body which are directly damaged by alcohol

1 ______________________________

2 ______________________________

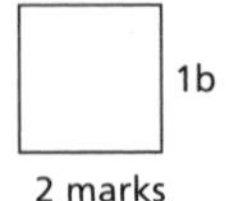
1b
2 marks

(c) Pure alcohol can be used to remove ink stains from fabric. If ink is the solute in this case, what is the name given to the alcohol?

1c
1 mark

____

(d) Alcohol will burn and can be used to heat water, etc. What does this suggest about alcohol?

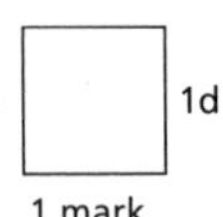
1d
1 mark

____

Maximum 6 marks

2. (a) The diagram below shows the female reproductive system.

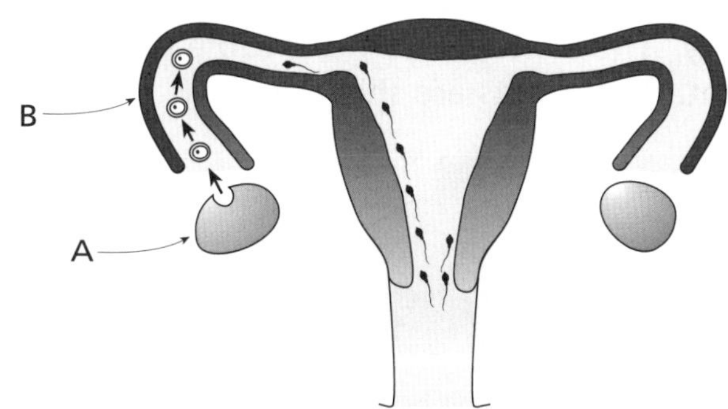

(i) What is the name given to the structure labelled A? 2ai 1 marks

____

(ii) What does structure A do? 2aii 1 mark

____

(iii) What is the name given to the structure labelled B? 2aiii 1 mark

____

(iv) What does structure B do? 2aiv 1 mark

____

(b) The diagram below shows an egg and a sperm.

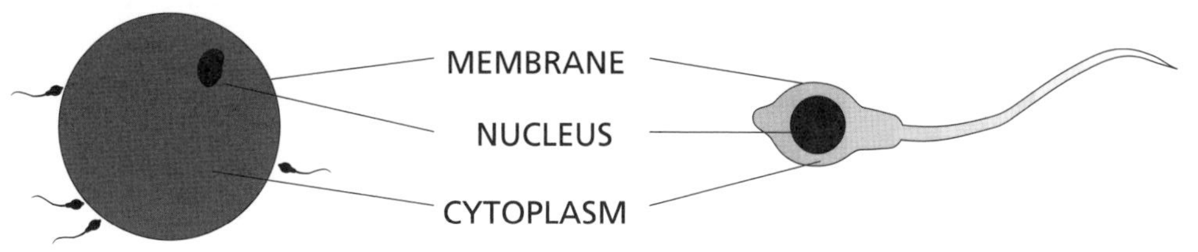

(i) Give one way in which the egg is adapted to perform its function. 2bi 1 mark

____

(ii) Give one way in which the sperm is adapted to perform its function. 2bii 1 mark

____

Maximum 6 marks

3. Pupils heated some magnesium ribbon inside a crucible until it burst into flames. The lid of the crucible was kept on most of the time but occasionally it lifted up briefly. The contents of the crucible were weighed before and after the experiment. The results are shown below.

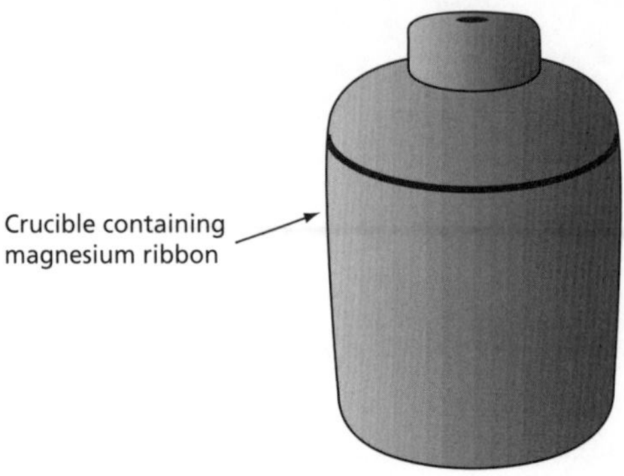

	Before (g)	After (g)
Mass of contents of crucible	2.40	3.90

After the experiment, the contents of the crucible consisted of a white ash.

(a) What is the white ash?

____

3a — 1 mark

(b) Write the word equation for the reaction which took place.

__________ + __________ → __________

3b — 1 mark

(c) What caused the increase in mass?

____

3c — 1 mark

(d) Why did the lid lift up occasionally during the experiment?

____

3d — 1 mark

(e)(i) If the experiment had been repeated without the lid, what effect would this have had on the mass of the contents of the crucible?

____

3ei — 1 mark

(ii) Explain your answer to (i).

____

3eii — 1 mark

Maximum 6 marks

4. The elements are arranged in the periodic table. The metallic elements and the non-metallic elements are roughly grouped together.

(a)(i) Name three metallic elements.

1 ______________________________

2 ______________________________

3 ______________________________

4ai 1 mark

(ii) Name one metallic element which is magnetic.

____

4aii 1 mark

(iii) Name a metallic element that is a liquid at room temperature.

____

4aiii 1 mark

(b)(i) Name three non-metallic elements

1 ______________________________

2 ______________________________

3 ______________________________

4bi 1 mark

(ii) Name one non-metallic element that is a gas at room temperature, is lighter than air and burns fiercely.

____

4bii 1 mark

(iii) Name one non-metallic element that is a solid at room temperature.

____

4biii 1 mark

Maximum 6 marks

5. The diagrams show the forces acting on three moving cars.

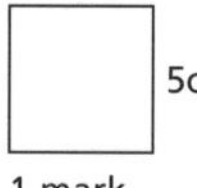
5a
2 marks

(a) On which car(s) are the forces acting unbalanced?

____

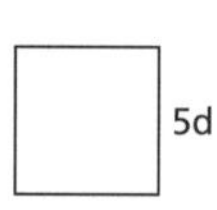
5b
1 mark

(b) On which car(s) are the forces acting balanced?

____

5c
1 mark

(c) Which car is speeding up?

____

5d
1 mark

(d) Which car is slowing down?

____

5e
1 mark

(e) Which car is moving at a steady speed?

____

Maximum 6 marks

6. (a) A car is travelling at a steady speed of 100km/h. Which of the following statements about the moving car are true? Tick the boxes next to the three correct answers.

(i) In 1 hour the car will travel a distance of 100km ☐

(ii) In 30 minutes the car will travel a distance of 100km ☐

(iii) In 2 hours the car will travel a distance of 200km ☐

(iv) In 30 minutes the car will travel a distance of 50km ☐

(v) In 100 minutes the car will travel a distance of 100km ☐

(vi) In 1 hour the car will travel a distance of 10km ☐

6a ☐ 3 marks

(b) A cyclist travels 80 metres in 40 seconds. Calculate the average speed of the cyclist and give your answer a unit.

____

____

____

6b ☐ 3 marks

Maximum 6 marks

7. (a) Complete the following sentences by filling in the gaps.

The two ends of a bar magnet are called ____________________ . One end is called the ________________-seeking pole and the other end is called the ________________-seeking pole.

7a
2 marks

(b) Look at the following diagrams of suspended magnets and read the statements underneath each one. For each example, write in the box underneath the diagram the polarity of end A.

(i)

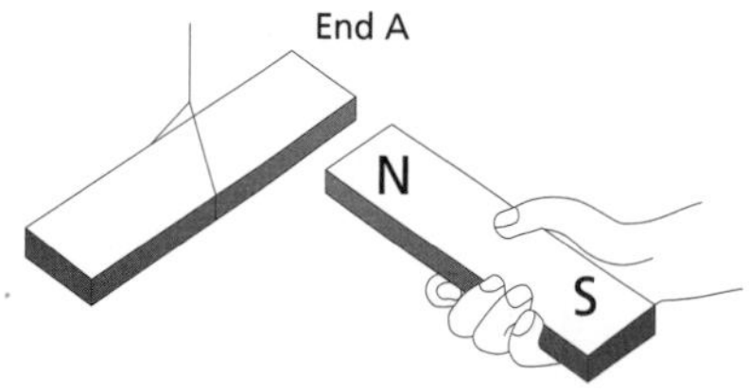

End A
N
S

The two magnets repel each other. End A is ____________________

7bi
1 mark

(ii)

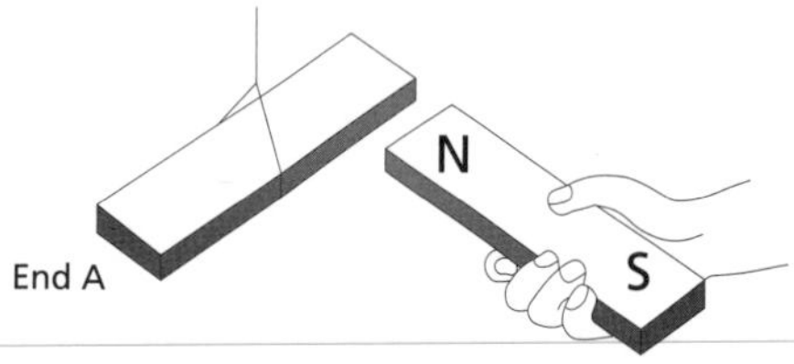

N
End A
S

The two magnets attract each other. End A is ____________________

7bii
1 mark

(iii)

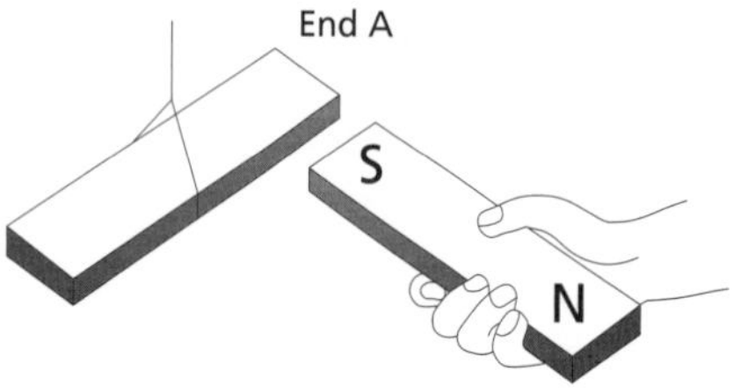

End A
S
N

The two magnets attract each other. End A is ____________________

7biii
1 mark

(iv)

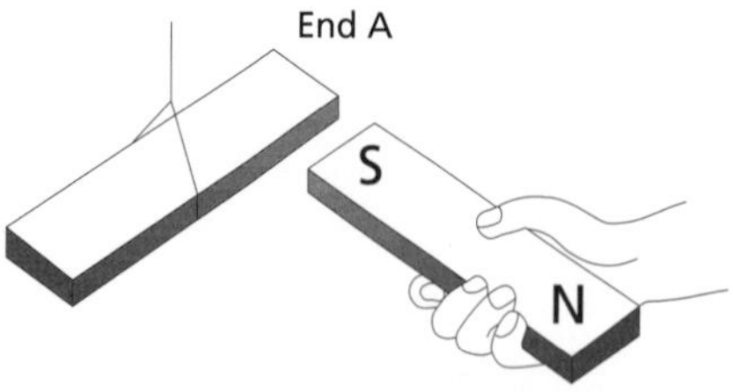

End A
S
N

The two magnets repel each other. End A is ____________________

7biv
1 mark

Maximum 6 marks

8. Some students decided to investigate what conditions woodlice prefer. Here is the equipment they used:

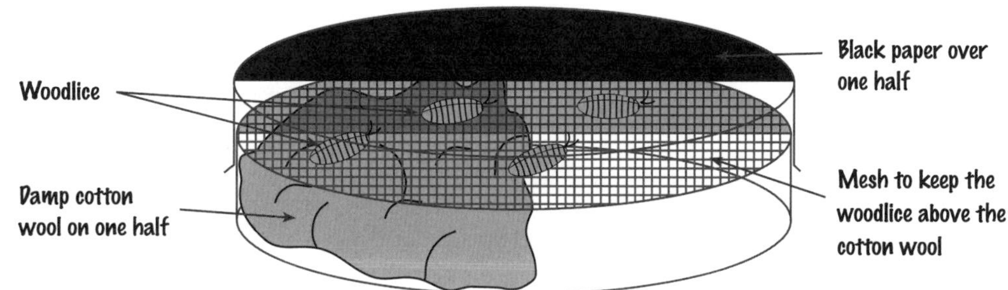

(a) Name two factors that must be kept the same in order to make this a fair test.

1 ______________________________

2 ______________________________

8a
2 marks

(b) The students obtained the following results by recording where the woodlice were every 2 minutes.

Time	0	2	4	6	8	10
Wet and dark	5	11	16	18	19	20
Wet and light	5	3	1	0	0	0
Dry and dark	5	4	3	2	1	0
Dry and light	5	2	0	0	0	0

(i) What conclusion can you draw from this investigation about where woodlice like to live?

____

8bi
1 mark

(ii) How many woodlice were used in this investigation?

____

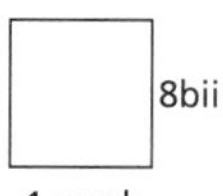

8bii
1 mark

(iii) What sort of conditions do woodlice like least?

____

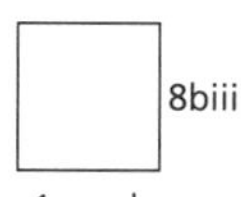

8biii
1 mark

(c) If this investigation had used only 4 woodlice, would the results have been as useful? Explain your answer.

____

8c
1 mark

Maximum 6 marks

9. (a) Complete the following passage by filling in the blanks.

Organisms of different species can be placed into groups based on their

observable ______________________ . Animals with backbones are called

____________________ , while those without backbones are called

____________________. Animals with backbones can be further subdivided

into mammals, birds, ____________________ , ______________________ and fish.

Only _______________ have hair and suckle their young.

9a
3 marks

(b)(i) Which animal group has a body divided into three parts, three pairs of legs, wings, an external skeleton and jointed legs?

____

9bi
1 mark

(ii) Which animal group can breathe through moist skin and needs water in order to breed?

____

9bii
1 mark

(iii) Which animal group has a body which is divided into segments, each one of which has bristles?

____

9biii
1 mark

Maximum 6 marks

10. A person's heart rate and breathing rate (ventilation rate) were monitored while they were in a resting position and then as they gradually increased the speed at which they were running. The following results were obtained.

Activity	Heart rate (beats per minute)	Ventilation rate (breaths per minute)
At rest	60	9
Walking	70	13
Slow jog	90	17
Steady jog	100	23
Fast jog	120	25
Nearly flat out	140	30
Flat out sprint	160	31

(a) Draw a line graph of these results on the graph paper below.

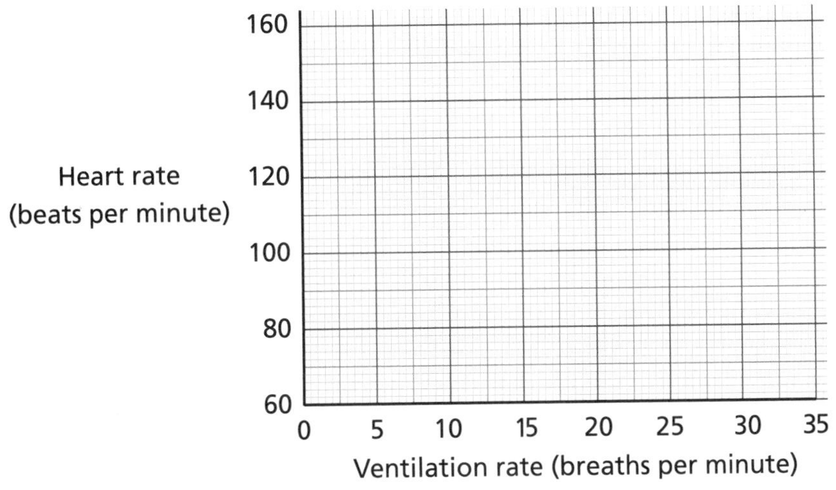

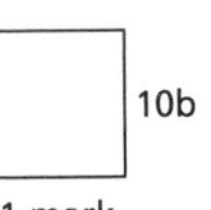

(b) Describe the link between heart rate and ventilation rate.

____

____

10b
1 mark

(c)(i) The heart and lungs form the cardiovascular system.
Name two things they supply to the working muscle tissue.

1 ____

2 ____

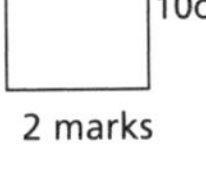

(ii) Name two things they remove from the working muscle tissue?

1 ____

2 ____

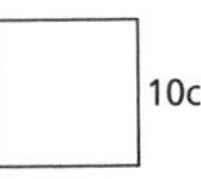

Maximum 6 marks

11. The table below gives data for the melting points and boiling points of 12 different elements.

Symbol of element	Na	Al	O	Ca	Hg	Au	He	Pb	S	Cu	Ni	K
Melting point °C	98	660	-219	840	-39	1064	-270	328	119	1083	1455	63
Boiling point °C	900	2400	-183	1490	357	2850	-269	1750	445	2580	2150	770

(a)(i) Which element(s) are solid at a room temperature of 20°C?

11ai
1 mark

(ii) Which element(s) are liquid at a room temperature of 20°C?

11aii
1 mark

(iii) Which element(s) are a gas at a room temperature of 20°C?

11aiii
1 mark

(b)(i) Which element has the biggest difference between its melting point and boiling point?

11bi
1 mark

(ii) Which element has the smallest difference between its melting point and boiling point?

11bii
1 mark

(c) Which element is a non-metallic solid at room temperature?

11c
1 mark

Maximum 6 marks

12. Some pupils performed an investigation into how salt affects the melting point of ice. Different amounts of salt were dissolved in water and then frozen to a temperature of -15°C. The ice was then crushed and placed in a filter funnel and the temperature noted as soon as the ice began to produce drips of water. The results are shown below.

Amount of salt (g)	0	5	10	15	20	25
Melting point of ice (°C)	0	-1	-3	-2	-10	-13

(a) Name three factors that must be carefully controlled in order to make this a fair test.

1 ______________________________

2 ______________________________

3 ______________________________

12a — 3 marks

(b) Which one of these results looks wrong?

____

12b — 1 mark

(c) What conclusion can you draw from this investigation?

____

12c — 1 mark

(d) Name one practical application of this conclusion that is used regularly in winter in this country.

____

12d — 1 mark

Maximum 6 marks

13. (a)(i) Acids and alkalis are often called 'chemical opposites'. Complete the following word equation to show what is produced when an acid is added to an alkali.

13ai

acid + alkali ⟶ ________________ + ________________

1 mark

(ii) Write a word equation to show an example of a reaction between an acid and an alkali.

13aii

____

1 mark

(iii) If the acid and alkali completely 'cancel each other out' so that the resulting solution is neutral, what will the pH be?

13aiii

____

1 mark

(b) A wasp sting can be treated by applying vinegar to it. What does this tell you about the pH of a wasp sting?

13b

____

1 mark

(c)(i) Acids react with metal carbonates. Complete the following word equation to show what is produced.

13ci

acid + metal carbonate ⟶ __________ + __________ + __________

1 mark

(ii) Write down a word equation to show an example of a reaction between an acid and a metal carbonate.

13cii

____

1 mark

Maximum 6 marks

14. A simple balance can be made like the one shown below.

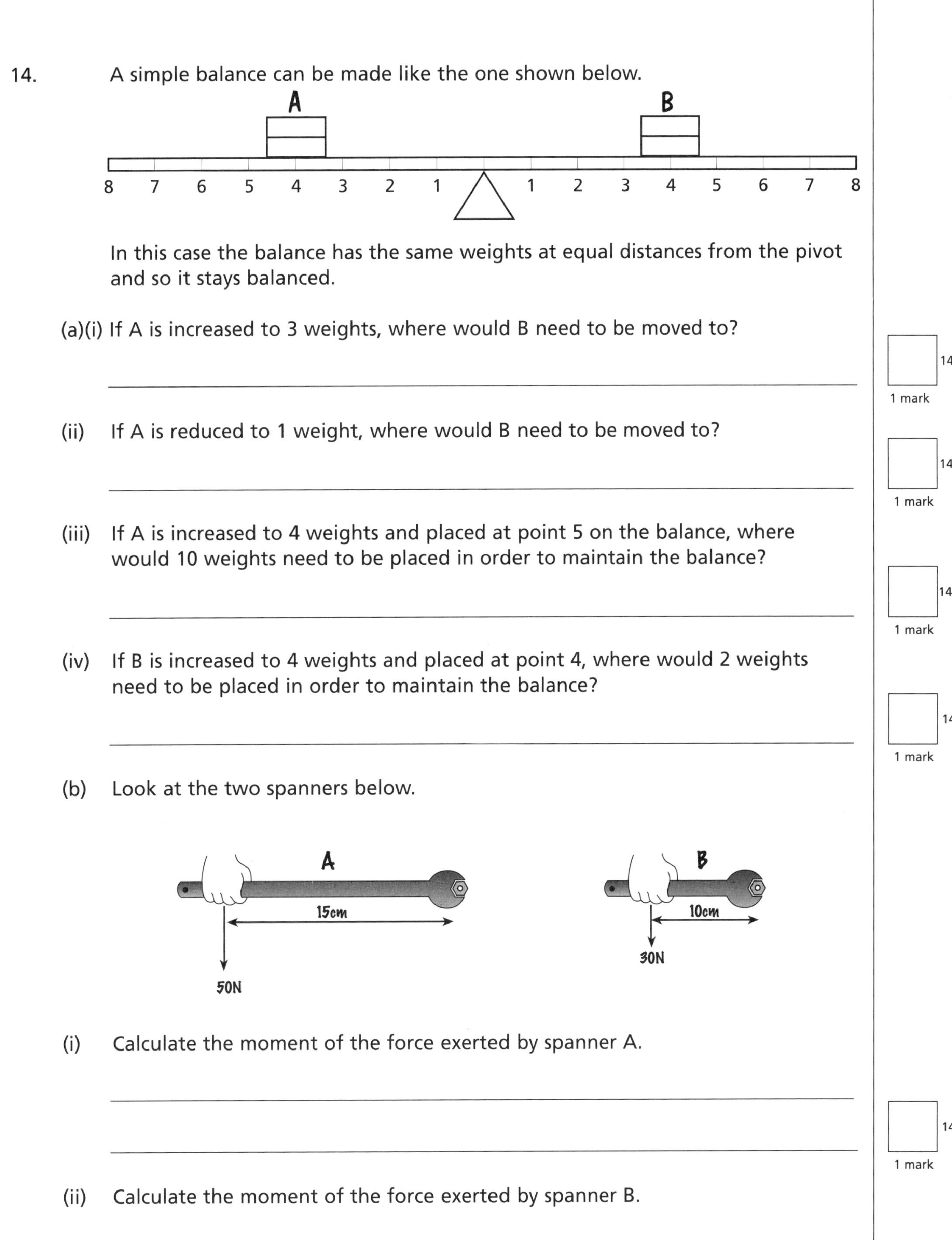

In this case the balance has the same weights at equal distances from the pivot and so it stays balanced.

(a)(i) If A is increased to 3 weights, where would B need to be moved to?

____

14ai 1 mark

(ii) If A is reduced to 1 weight, where would B need to be moved to?

____

14aii 1 mark

(iii) If A is increased to 4 weights and placed at point 5 on the balance, where would 10 weights need to be placed in order to maintain the balance?

____

14aiii 1 mark

(iv) If B is increased to 4 weights and placed at point 4, where would 2 weights need to be placed in order to maintain the balance?

____

14aiv 1 mark

(b) Look at the two spanners below.

(i) Calculate the moment of the force exerted by spanner A.

____

____

14bi 1 mark

(ii) Calculate the moment of the force exerted by spanner B.

____

____

14bii 1 mark

Maximum 6 marks

15. (a) Energy can exist in many forms. List three common forms of energy.

1 ______

2 ______

3 ______

15a
3 marks

(b) Coal, oil and gas can be used to produce electricity. Rearrange the following statements to show the order of the process.

A Turbines turn the generator

B Boiling water turns to steam

C Heat from burning fuel is used to boil water

D Steam turns the turbines

E Generator produces electricity

☐ → ☐ → ☐ → ☐ → ☐

15b
2 marks

(c) What is the original source of most energy resources?

______

15c
1 mark

Maximum 6 marks

Our Student Workbook matches the Revision Guide page for page and provides great reinforcement and excellent homework material.

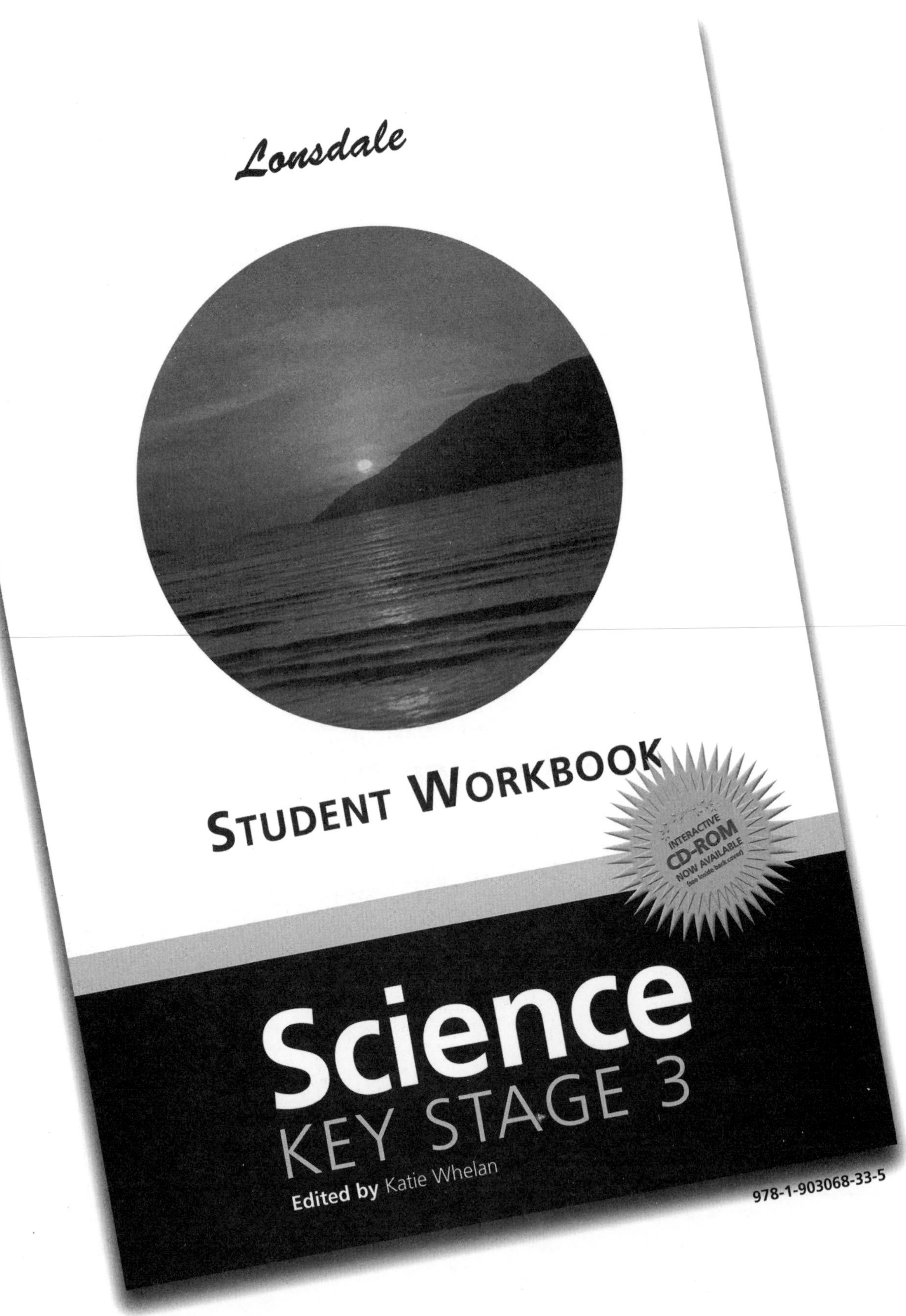